CW00665334

Extensions of Time Explained

Extensions of Time Explained

Gillian Birkby and Paul Brough

Published by RIBA Publications Ltd
Finsbury Mission, Moreland Street, London EC1V 8BB

RIBA Publications is the publishing company of
the Royal Institute of British Architects

ISBN 0 947877 97 5

Editor: Alaine Hamilton
Book design and computer page make-up: Penny Mills
Printed and bound by Biddles Ltd, Guildford

Whilst every effort has been made to check the accuracy of the information given in this book, readers should always make their own checks. Neither the author nor the publisher accepts any responsibility for mis-statements made in it or misunderstandings arising from it.

The various personae in this book are referred to as 'he', purely as a matter of stylistic simplicity.

Contents

Preface

Delays to completion are such a common feature of building projects that it is essential for construction professionals to understand how they are dealt with in standard building contracts. *Extensions of Time Explained* offers guidance to all contract administrators called upon to grapple with the assessment of delay and its various causes. This is a complex area of contract administration and it is not surprising that many claims for extensions of time have been argued out in the courts; the book includes discussion of the relevant case law and its application to the clauses in the JCT standard forms and the Government forms of building contract. To simplify the variety of terminology used, we have referred throughout to the contract administrator rather than architect or project manager. The jurisdiction considered is the law of England and Wales.

From the joint perspective of solicitor and quantity surveyor, in section 6 we offer a detailed methodology for the assessment of delay, and in the concluding section, 'Common problems', we answer some of the questions that often arise in relation to extensions of time.

We should like to thank colleagues in our respective firms for their support and advice, and our ever-willing and long-suffering secretaries, Ann Smith and Sheila Hammond.

Gillian Birkby
Paul Brough
July 1993

Glossary

Act of prevention: An event which delays practical completion of a building contract, is caused by or on behalf of the employer, and to which the extensions of time clause does not apply.

***Contra proferentem*:** A Latin term meaning 'against the person putting [it] forward'. It is a rule of law adopted when considering a contract which contains an ambiguity of wording. The contract is interpreted against the interests of the person drawing it up, or who would benefit from it.

Critical path: The sequence of stages in a building programme which must follow each other sequentially, each of which depends on the completion of the previous stage, and all of which are essential in order to achieve practical completion by the date for completion.

Culpable delay: A contractor is in culpable delay when the contractual completion date has passed without practical completion having been achieved, and the contract administrator does not consider that the contractor is entitled to a further extension of time.

Dotting-on: The dot-on principle is a method of granting extensions of time by adding the time attributable to the delaying event to the existing contractual completion date, thereby extending it for the period attributable to that delay.

***Obiter [dictum]*:** A category of statement made by a judge as part of his judgment, which is not necessary for the decision in a particular case, and which therefore carries less force when considering the statement as a precedent for later cases.

SMM7: The Standard Method of Measurement of Building Works, Seventh Edition, published by the Royal Institution of Chartered Surveyors and the Building Employers' Confederation.

Time at large: A situation where the contractual date for completion no longer applies, usually because the contract has been delayed by the employer for a reason which is not covered by an extensions of time clause. See also para. 2.18.

1 Introduction

1.01 Building contracts are by their very nature complex, involving a whole host of different trades and professions. The trend in recent years has been to use an increasing number of sub-contractors to carry out the actual work, and it is not uncommon to have 30 or 40 different companies working on a construction site during the course of the project. The difficulties of completing on time are compounded by the fact that the decision as to how long a project should take is often made casually by the design team, more by instinct and experience than by careful calculation. Added to this, there are frequently events, large and small, which threaten the smooth running of the project: unforeseen ground conditions, freak weather, an adjoining owner taking out an injunction to prevent out-of-hours working. Given this complexity, and the potential for delays to occur, it is perhaps surprising that any project is ever completed on time.

1.02 It is to be expected, then, that some provision should be made in the commonly used forms of contract to provide a way of dealing with delays which are likely to affect the completion date. This is particularly important for the employer, whose ability to claim liquidated and ascertained damages if he causes a delay may be affected if there is no mechanism for an extension to be given. The standard forms all recognise that there should be a date set for the completion of the project, and at the same time that the completion date might be put back by the contract administrator granting an extension of the time originally allowed to achieve completion of the project.

1.03 Those who contract under a non-standard form may not be so lucky. Kitsons, the insulation sub-contractor for Matthew Hall in the erection of Terminal 4 at Heathrow, discovered this to their cost. Kitsons had accepted an order from Matthew Hall which stated: 'Work to be carried out in accordance with the dictates [or instructions] of our site management team, to enable the overall mechanical services to be complete and handed over to our client on 18.3.85.' Matthew Hall were also to secure availability and access to site areas so far as they were able. In the event, Kitsons were late in completing their work and Matthew Hall refused to grant an extension of time. Kitsons said that they were delayed by Matthew Hall's failure to make work available, as required by the revised programme which had been issued. The judge held that both parties must have recognised that the prospects of being able to work closely to a programme were small, and that as long as Matthew Hall tried to obtain access to areas needed by Kitsons, they were not in breach of contract even if the programme was not adhered to and Kitsons were, on occasions, unable to do any work at all because of lack of access.

1.04 This case illustrates the way in which contracts are interpreted by the English courts and is of particular significance when considering claims for extensions of time. The exact wording is crucial. It is essential, in the case of the one-off, non-standard form of contract, to read the contract carefully so as to appreciate the implications of the various provisions. For Kitsons, in the case mentioned above, the extensions of time clause was no help at all, because the work itself had to be done on an 'as required' basis and there was no guarantee that they would be given the access to carry out the work in the way they had anticipated when they tendered. A similar difficulty can arise when a standard form is used, but one party has made adjustments to some of the clauses without realising how this will affect the operation of other clauses in the contract. Building contracts can be as complex as the building work itself and should be amended only with great care and after considerable thought.

1.05 Most of this book is devoted to a study of extensions of time and the clauses by which those extensions can be granted. *Kitsons v Matthew Hall* is an example of an extensions of time clause which did not work because of other clauses in the contract. Sometimes the situation is even more serious and the whole contractual edifice collapses, as in the case of *Croudace v London Borough of Lambeth*. In that case Lambeth's chief architect was the named contract administrator in the contract. Having granted an extension of time, that individual subsequently retired and no one was appointed to take his place. There was therefore no one to certify loss and expense arising out of the extension as required by the terms of the contract (which in that case was JCT 63). The court held that the failure to appoint someone else as contract administrator for the purposes of the contract was a breach of contract by Lambeth, which subsequently entitled Croudace to recover their loss and expense as damages for breach of contract, rather than as loss and expense itself. The situation would arguably have been the same if the contract administrator had retired before granting an extension of time. Again, the exact wording of the contract was crucial, and it was Lambeth's failure to comply with their obligation to appoint a contract administrator under the contract which caused them such difficulties.

1.06 Extensions of time can only ultimately be fully understood in the context of the particular contract in which the provision appears. Everything will depend upon the exact wording used and any amendments made, whether to the extensions of time clause or to other relevant parts of the contract. In approaching the subject for the purposes of this book, therefore, time constraints which feature in building contracts have been considered, including the general purpose and function of the extensions of time clause, the types of delay usually found and the typical elements of an extensions of time clause. The way in which delay is to be assessed, and problems which frequently arise in doing so, are to some extent common whichever of the standard forms is used, and these also form the subject of separate sections within the book. For convenience, because it is probably the most familiar of the forms, the JCT Standard Form of Building Contract (JCT 80) is used as an example unless an alternative form is mentioned.

2 Time in building contracts

The contract period

2.01 In theory at least, all construction contracts have a beginning and an end, and the period between is usually decided upon before invitations to tender are sent to prospective contractors. In recent years there has been an increasing use of forms of contract which are fast track, i.e. which shorten the overall period from the commencement of design up to practical completion of the work on site. In most cases, this is achieved by overlapping the design and construction phases rather than reducing the overall construction period, although there have been some inroads here also. There are some indications now of a recognition that speed is not always compatible with quality, and certainly not compatible with tight financial constraints.

2.02 The degree of sophistication of a contractor's programme for the period of construction varies widely, ranging from an outline scheme to a detailed analysis of what each sub-contractor should be doing on any particular day. Of the standard forms of contract only GC/Works/1/ Edition 3 allows for the contractor's programme to become one of the contract documents, defining the sequence in which the works are to be carried out. The result of this is that, for most contracts, although the contractor has an end date to which he is working, he has a great deal of flexibility in determining the order of work, and the exact timing of each individual part. The contractor's obligation is usually limited to the requirement that he should commence the works on the date for commencement and thereafter proceed 'regularly and diligently'. If he does that, and completes on time, he will not be in breach of contract if he does not actually adhere to his own programme. It follows that if the timing of the different parts of the works results in added expenditure to the employer, for instance by entitling the contractor to higher rates to reflect greater inflation for work carried out later in the contract period, the employer can do nothing about this, and must pay the extra costs incurred. This was the case in *GLC v Cleveland Bridge*, where Cleveland Bridge were employed to manufacture, supply and install the gates and gate arms for the Thames Barrier. The contract set out certain key dates by which various parts of the works had to be completed, and Cleveland Bridge complied with these. At the same time, the employer had to pay more in fluctuations for inflation costs than he anticipated, because of the sequence Cleveland Bridge had adopted for the different parts of the works. It was held that this was not a breach of contract; Cleveland Bridge were entitled to organise the progress of the works as they saw fit.

2.03 Another common feature of a contractor's programme is that it will show that the contractor plans to finish the work early, i.e. before the completion date. The question then arises, is the contract administrator obliged to perform his role under the building contract in supplying information, supplementary drawings etc in such a way as to enable the contrator to achieve early completion? This was considered in the case of *Glenlion v Guinness Trust*, where it was held that although Glenlion were entitled to complete before the date for completion and to carry out the works in order to achieve that earlier date, there was no parallel obligation on the contract administrator to provide information to enable the contractor to achieve his earlier date. If there had been, this would have had the effect of imposing on the employer an earlier completion date. Although in some circumstances an employer might welcome this, it might equally cause some difficulty if the employer had made his funding arrangements on the basis of a longer programme.

2.04 In theory, then, the contractor has considerable scope in deciding on the order in which the works will be carried out, and the timing of the individual parts. In practice, however, progress will be monitored closely both by the contractor, so that he can make his claims for extensions of time if that is appropriate, and also by the professional team, who, like the contractor, realise the need for the work to proceed in an orderly fashion. This is necessary in order to ensure the appropriate standard of quality and to avoid serious disputes arising at the end of the job over whether practical completion has been achieved.

2.05 There is usually nothing in a building contract which expressly entitles the contract administrator to interfere with the contractor's rate of progress, although some of the forms do have provision for acceleration, with the contractor's consent, and overtime rates are often required as part of the contractor's tender, in anticipation of overtime working. In practice the contractor will usually present a monthly progress report at site meetings, and there will be discussions between the contractor and the professional team about the rate of progress, why there has been or will be delay, how lost time is to be made up, and whether delays in different parts of the works will have an effect on the completion date – some delays may not be critical.

Commencement

2.06 Sometimes the completion date is expressed as being 'x weeks after the date for possession', which is usually intended to mean the commencement of work on site. This is unlikely to be the same as the date of execution of the building contract. Ideally, the contract should be executed under hand, i.e. signed (or executed as a deed) before work starts on site and not, as is often the case, just before practical completion. Working without a formal contract or merely on a letter of intent can cause problems to both parties, and may give rise to argument whether the conditions of contract which incorporate the extensions of time clause form part of the agreement between the parties at all.

2.07 It is a good idea to record, at the first site meeting, the date on which work started on site, since this is often not clear from any other document and may be of importance later if the completion date is fixed by reference to it. It must be distinguished from the date on which off-site work commenced, for instance prefabrication or the ordering of long delivery items. It is quite common for the contractor to be allowed on the site 'early' in order to set up site huts etc, and again it is helpful if there is some record of whether or not this period is to be considered part of the contract period.

2.08 Where the contract is carried out in phases or sections, it is even more important to record the date on which the contractor has been granted possession of each phase, and the date on which he is expected to complete each of the phases. In paras. 7.01–7.07 there is a more detailed discussion of sectional completion.

Completion

2.09 It may be a cliché to say that time is money, but when applied to a building contract it is particularly apt. For the employer, the sooner the building is finished the sooner he can move into occupation or let it so that it can generate rental income (in theory at least). For the contractor, the sooner he completes the work the sooner he can move his men and materials off site, and the greater his profit will be where he is working to a fixed price contract, which is the most common situation. In short, it is important for both parties to decide in advance when and how soon the project will be completed. This explains why in construction contracts there is invariably a date for completion set, as the point at which the project is to be ready for handing over to the employer. Very often this date for completion (although not necessarily the contract period) will change between the date on which invitations to tender are sent out, when the date for completion will be included in the documents, and the date on which work commences on site. It is important that there should be no confusion over this date.

2.10 For most building contracts, the date for completion current at the time work commences on site is usually the operative one, and it is important that this date is the one inserted into the contract documents, if they have not already been signed by the time work starts on site. There is some recognition that this date may change during the tender period in the new documents for use with nominated sub-contractors under JCT 80 which were introduced by Amendment 10 to JCT 80. Since the operation of the extensions of time clause depends upon an undisputed, initial contractual date for completion, it is clearly essential that this date be inserted in the contract, or failing that, is recorded in correspondence or in the minutes of a meeting.

2.11 In theory at least, the contractor's programme for the works will be related to the date for completion. The fixing of the date is therefore of benefit not only to the employer, so that he knows when he can expect the project to be handed over to him, but also to the contractor, who can plan his work and that of his sub-contractors. It will be his aim to achieve that date for completion without incurring extra expenditure in, for instance, overtime working which has not been included as part of his tender, and for which he may not be reimbursed.

Failure to complete on time

2.12 Having entered into a building contract with a set date for completion, if the contractor has not achieved practical completion by that date, certain consequences follow. The basic principles have been helpfully set out by the House of Lords in *Percy Bilton v GLC* as follows:

'1. The general rule is that the main contractor is bound to complete the work by the date for completion stated in the contract. If he fails to do so, he will be liable for liquidated damages to the employer.

2. That is subject to the exception that the employer is not entitled to liquidated damages if by his acts or omissions he has prevented the main contractor from completing his work by the completion date.

3. These general rules may be amended by the express terms of the contract.'

2.13 Liquidated and ascertained damages are a sum of money, usually expressed on a weekly or daily basis, which, at the outset of the contract, the employer states will be his loss if the project does not achieve practical completion on time. This is a complex subject, and it is sufficient to say here that a failure by the contractor to achieve completion by the due date is a breach of contract, for which the employer is entitled to damages. As the House of Lords pointed out in *Bilton*, if the employer has by his own acts or omissions prevented the main contractor from completing on time, he will not be entitled to liquidated damages as set out in the contract, unless the contract provides otherwise. However, to avoid an employer losing his remedy of liquidated damages where the employer has delayed the contractor, the extensions of time clause amends the general rule by providing that in certain circumstances an extension of time for completion can be granted to the contractor, thus preserving the employer's right to liquidated damages if the contractor is still late in completing after the extended period has elapsed. When an employer has delayed the contract for reasons not covered by the extensions of time clause, this is often referred to as an 'act of prevention' by the employer.

2.14 It is important to realise that the extensions of time clause is primarily for the benefit of the employer, so that he can preserve his right to operate the liquidated damages clause and has some quick and convenient remedy against the contractor if there is a delay in completion attributable to the contractor himself.

Making time of the essence

2.15 Failure to comply with a contractual obligation does not normally entitle the aggrieved party to terminate the contract unless the time for performance of that obligation has been made 'of the essence'. If the parties to a contract wish to make time of the essence, they can do so in relation to certain specific terms of the contract, e.g. the date for completion, but not in relation to the contract as a whole. The consequences are that if the party which is under the obligation to complete fails to do so by the required date, the other party can treat the contract as having been repudiated, which will release him from any obligation to carry out his own part of the contract.

2.16 In order to make time of the essence for a particular requirement in a contract, express words must be used to show that this is the intention. The structure of a building contract, which usually contains an extensions of time clause and a liquidated damages clause, does not make time of the essence in relation to the contractor's obligation to achieve practical completion by a certain date. Nevertheless, if the employer wished to do so, he could serve notice on the contractor requiring completion by a certain date, and provided this were properly worded, it would have the effect of making time of the essence.

2.17 There are various reasons why, in a building contract, time is not generally of the essence. The purpose of such a requirement is to entitle the employer to terminate the contract and bring a claim for damages when completion is late, and in many cases it will not be in the interests of the employer to do so. The employer already has his remedy in liquidated damages if the contractor is in delay. Moreover, on most building contracts it will be quicker and cheaper to allow the existing contractor to finish the work, albeit late, than to dismiss him and employ another contractor who will not be familiar with the building or the works which are to be carried out. There are also many cases where practical completion is not achieved by the completion date, but it is not clear at that stage whether the contractor may be entitled to further extensions of time. Several of the standard forms allow the contract administrator a further period after practical completion in which to make his final decision on extensions of time. In those circumstances it would be premature for the employer to allege that the contractor's failure to complete by the completion date was a repudiation of the contract; if the employer did so, and the contract administrator subsequently decided that a further extension was warranted, the employer could find that he himself was guilty of repudiation of the building contract and that the contractor was entitled to damages for wrongful repudiation. The standard forms, with their provisions for extensions of time and liquidated damages, are designed to avoid this particular legal minefield.

Time at large

2.18 Contractors who are already in delay often try to turn this to their advantage by claiming that time is at large. 'Time at large' is used to describe a position where some event has occurred during the course of the contract, usually causing delay, for which the extensions of time clause contains no provision. If the act in question can be classed as an act of prevention by the employer, its effect will be to invalidate the date set for completion. Since it does not fall within the terms of the extensions of time clause, the contract administrator cannot grant an extension, and the contractor is then under an obligation merely to complete within a reasonable time and not by the completion date provided in the contract. For example, if the employer delayed in granting possession of the site to the contractor for seven weeks beyond the date for commencement in the contract (and bearing in mind that the maximum allowed for this purpose under the JCT contracts is six weeks) the contract administrator would have no power to grant a further extension of time. If the parties did not amend the contract by agreeing a new possession date and a new completion date, arguably time would be at large and the contractor would only be required to complete within a reasonable time, even though commonsense would suggest that the completion date should merely be extended by seven weeks to allow for the delay in commencement on site.

2.19 There used to be an argument that time may also be put at large if the contract administrator fails to grant an extension of time within the period set down in the building contract. Most JCT contracts now contain a provision allowing the contract administrator a further 12 weeks after practical completion in which to review his extensions. It is less likely, therefore, that time will become at large simply because the contract administrator does not grant an extension which has been applied for during the course of the works. This subject is discussed in more detail in paras. 7.08–7.13.

Sub-contractors

2.20 The position of sub-contractors on building contracts is particularly difficult, since they must coordinate the timing of their own work with that of the main contractor and other sub-contractors. The difficulties experienced by Kitsons in their contract with Matthew Hall have already been mentioned in para. 1.03. In that case, the contractor was held not liable to Kitsons for failure to grant access to any particular part of the works so that they could complete their sub-contract works. The earlier case of *Martin Grant v Sir Lindsay Parkinson* was just as difficult. Again, a non-standard form of sub-contract had been used and the court held that there was no implied term that the main contractor would make sufficient work available to the sub-contractors to enable them to maintain reasonable progress and to execute their work in an efficient and economic manner. Nor was there an implied term that the main contractor would not hinder or prevent the sub-contractors in the execution of the sub-contract works. It was recognised that there may be an implied obligation for parties in contract with each other to cooperate, but 'the degree of cooperation will depend ... upon the express terms of any contract which the parties may have made'.

2.21 Where a standard form of sub-contract has been used, for instance the nominated sub-contract conditions under JCT 80, there is a provision (clause 2.1) which states: 'the contractor shall give to the sub-contractor sufficient information on the progress of the works to enable him to fulfill his obligations [to carry out the sub-contract works in accordance with the agreed programme details and reasonably in accordance with the progress of the works].' In a recent case on the domestic form of sub-contract for use with

WCD 81 (DOM/2), the contractor and sub-contractor agreed that there was an implied term in the sub-contract that the contractor would provide the sub-contractor with correct information concerning the works. The court held that the implied obligation extended to the provision of such information 'in such a manner and at such times as was reasonably necessary for the [sub-contractor] to have in order for it to fulfill its obligations under the sub-contract'. *(J & J Fee Limited v Express Lift Company Limited)*

2.22 In general terms, domestic sub-contractors under the standard forms are entitled to extensions of time from the main contractor for similar reasons to those set out in the main contract. The position of nominated sub-contractors under JCT 80 is slightly different: an application for an extension of time for a nominated sub-contractor must receive the consent of the architect before the contractor can grant it.

2.23 When one of his sub-contractors causes delay, the consequences for the contractor will depend on the exact terms of the various contracts. The general rule is that a contractor is entirely liable for his sub-contractors, and if they cause delay he can only obtain an extension of time if that delay falls within one of the categories which entitle the contractor himself to an extension. However, there are some exceptions. Under JCT 80, for instance, clause 25.4.7 allows an extension of time for the contractor where there has been delay by a nominated sub-contractor. That clause does not, however, include the situation, now all too common, where the sub-contractor has ceased work on site, whether by reason of insolvency or otherwise. In those circumstances, the complex provisions of clause 35 of JCT 80 will apply, which in essence provide that the contractor will be entitled to an extension of time if he suffers delay as a result of a re-nomination instruction for the appointment of a new nominated sub-contractor.

2.24 Where the contractor has engaged domestic sub-contractors, he is not entitled to an extension of time on account of their delay unless that delay falls within one of the express categories set out in the extensions of time clause, or the contract allows it. IFC 84, for example, makes special provision for named sub-contractors where they fail to finish their works, so that in those circumstances the contractor will sometimes be entitled to an extension of time, even though they are classed as domestic sub-contractors.

Alternative approaches

2.25 Extensions of time and liquidated damages are one way of dealing with possible failure by the contractor to complete on time, but there are other approaches which are sometimes used. For example, a contract might provide for acceleration where progress appears to be falling behind, or the contractor might be offered legitimate incentives to complete in the shortest possible time ahead of the completion date. Standard forms of building contract seldom include such terms, but they are not uncommon in non-standard forms.

ACCELERATION

2.26 The JCT Management Contract (MC 87) and GC/Works/1 Edition 3 both make specific provision for acceleration of the contract works. In MC 87 the clause is subject to the consent of the contractor, and in both forms it is envisaged that the cost of acceleration will be pre-priced. This is important, since acceleration is inevitably an expensive procedure, requiring careful resequencing of the works. It is not sufficient simply to employ more labour on site since this can easily be counter-productive, particularly when work has to be carried out in relatively confined spaces. The cost of acceleration makes it a last resort in most cases.

LANE RENTALS

2.27 This is an example of an incentive approach. The contractor notionally rents the stretch of motorway or highway which is the subject of the construction contract, the cost of the rental being repaid to the contractor by means of an adjustment to the contract price. The contractor has an incentive to complete the work as quickly as possible in order to avoid further payments of the rental. The concept is not particularly appropriate for complex building work, where it is recognised that the contract administrator may have to provide further information as the work proceeds and variations are common. The stick of liquidated damages rather than the carrot of a rental system is therefore more appropriate for this kind of project.

MILESTONE OR KEY DATES

2.28 These are interim dates written into the contract, and are contractually imposed deadlines by which the contractor is to have completed certain parts of the works. This differs from sectional completion, in that the various parts of the works involved are not sections which would allow the employer to take possession of them but merely stages in the construction process, e.g. completion of ground works, waterproof envelope etc. Interim payments are linked to completion of the various stages, and if the dates are not met an additional retention may be made until the contractor is back on programme. The purpose of imposing interim dates is to exert greater control over the contractor's progress during the course of the works. Otherwise, the contract administrator would have to wait until the date on which practical completion should have been achieved before being able to impose any sanction on the contractor for delay.

2.29 Any attempt to incorporate this concept into the standard forms should be approached with some care, since inexpert drafting can impose a sanction which is unenforceable. For further information, see the article on this subject by A. Houghton in *Construction Law Journal* 1992 Vol.8 No.3, which discusses the need to deal with legitimate claims for extensions of time which may affect the achievement of the key dates, and other drafting pitfalls.

OMISSIONS

2.30 Where a contractor is clearly in delay, the employer might consider omitting some part of the work. This may be particularly important where the employer needs to take occupation. Where the contract administrator orders omissions, he can at the same time shorten the period to practical completion if this is appropriate, but only as far as the original completion date. Under most contracts the contract administrator is not entitled to reduce the contract period so as to make it shorter than the original period.

2.31 The basic rule is that a contractor is entitled to carry out the work originally forming part of the contract or instructed subsequently. The employer cannot omit part of the works with the intention of instructing a different contractor. However, this does not prevent the employer from changing his mind about the type of construction he requires or ordering omissions to save costs.

3 Extensions of time clauses

3.01 In theory, an employer could impose an absolute obligation on the contractor to complete by a certain date whatever delaying circumstances arose during the course of the contract. He could then go on to impose liquidated damages for failure to meet the completion date. If a contractor was asked to tender for that kind of contract, however, he would inevitably increase his price to reflect the increased risk of having to pay some liquidated damages for delay. The extensions of time clause in a building contract allocates the risk of non-completion and reduces the contractor's risk in relation to delays by entitling him to an extension of time for completion in various circumstances, thus putting back the date on which liquidated damages will start to apply. Such a clause is therefore beneficial to a contractor. In most of the standard forms there is a further benefit, in that the actual cost of the extended period on site, e.g. the cost of the site set up, may be paid by the employer, although there is no direct connection between the extensions of time clause and the clause entitling the contractor to further money where there is delay.

3.02 Delay can be divided into two broad categories: delay to completion of the contract itself, resulting from a delay to work which is on the critical path of the construction programme, and delay to a part of the work which does not cause delay to overall completion, i.e. non-critical delay. Obviously, extensions of time are concerned with the first type of delay.

3.03 The function of an extensions of time clause, in assisting an employer, has already been discussed in paras. 2.13 and 2.14. If the employer causes delay to a contract for any reason, for instance by requiring a variation to the contract works, unless there is express provision in the contract allowing an extended completion date to be fixed to take account of that delay, the delaying event would be classed as an act of prevention by the employer, preventing the contractor from complying with his contractual obligation to complete by a certain date. The act in question must, however, be the responsibility of the employer. In the *Bilton* case (mentioned in paras. 2.12 and 2.13) the event had nothing to do with the employer, but concerned the insolvency of a nominated sub-contractor who failed to complete his work on site. The contract made no provision for extensions of time in these circumstances and the House of Lords held that, since there was no express entitlement for the contractor to receive an extension of time, the basic rule applied, which was that the contractor must take responsibility for this delay. If it had been classed as a default of the employer, time would have become at large, and the contractor would only have been obliged to complete within a reasonable time.

3.04 If the employer does commit an act of prevention, thereby putting time at large, there is no reason, in theory, why the employer should not be able to apply the liquidated damages clause after the expiry of the reasonable time allowed for completion, if the contractor has still failed to complete. However, the exact wording of the liquidated damages clause will usually prevent the employer from taking advantage of it, because it will refer to an original completion date which no longer applies. The employer is therefore entitled only to unliquidated damages, i.e. he must prove what losses he has suffered as a result of the delay by the contractor. It is important to note that even if there has been an act of prevention by the employer, the contractor must still complete within a reasonable time. If there are any delays in completion for reasons which would normally be the responsibility of the contractor, he is still liable for any loss caused to the employer by those delays (*Peak v McKinney*).

3.05 If a contractor alleges there has been an act of prevention by the employer, the contract administrator is faced with a dilemma. Should he continue to administer the contract and grant extensions of time as and when he considers these appropriate, or should he accept the contractor's allegation and leave the contractor to complete in what he considers to be a 'reasonable time'? In most circumstances it is probably best for the contract administrator to continue to administer the contract. In the first place, the contractor's allegation may not be correct, in which case the contract administrator still has the obligation and the power to grant extensions of time. In addition, even if the contractor is correct, the contract administrator's assessment on extensions of time will be useful in subsequently deciding whether the contractor did complete within a reasonable time. Another factor is that contracts tend to take longer to complete where there is no clear end date. By issuing extensions of time as appropriate during the course of the contract, the contract administrator is helping to maintain the momentum of the contract.

3.06 As discussed in paras 2.13 and 2.14, the extensions of time clause enables the employer to preserve his right to operate the liquidated damages clause. For the contractor, the extensions of time clause allows extra time in which to complete the work and, in some circumstances, may also form the basis of a claim for extra payment. Of course, the contractor can be entitled to extra payment because of variations, disturbance etc whether or not there has been any delay.

3.07 There are two fundamentally different approaches to the drafting of extensions of time clauses. The JCT contracts (apart from MW 80) set out a long list of specific events which may entitle the contractor to extensions of time. In JCT 80, by Amendment 13, variations for which the contractor has provided a quotation in advance are to be instructed together with their extensions of time, if appropriate, and are not dealt with under the extensions of time clause (see para 4.23). This can be contrasted with GC/Works/1 Edition 3 clause 36, which lists certain events in very general terms, including 'the act, neglect or default of the Authority or the PM' and then contains a 'sweep up' clause:

'any other circumstances (other than weather conditions) which are outside the control of the Contractor or any of his sub-contractors and which could not have been reasonably contemplated under the Contract.'

3.08 The Government form is drafted so as to avoid any arguments about acts of prevention by the employer, whereas the JCT forms do not entirely exclude that possibility. The JCT wording imposes a certain discipline on employers to operate within the express confines of the contract. This may be of advantage to employers when obtaining tenders because contractors can see exactly what kinds of delaying events are envisaged and should not therefore increase their tenders to allow for contingencies in this respect. In the case of projects under the Government form, political events or security reasons may dictate the pace of work on site, and the more general wording of GC/Works/1 gives greater scope for granting extensions where appropriate, avoiding the risk of time becoming at large. The sweep-up clause may give rise to argument on what 'could not have been reasonably contemplated under the Contract' but gives a wide discretion to the contract administrator.

3.09 MW 80 deals with extensions of time in a much simplified manner, with one all-embracing clause. The events which might give rise to an extension of time are not listed, and the criterion is simply that 'the works will not be completed by the date for completion ... for reasons beyond the control of the contractor'. The contractor is to notify the contract administrator, who will then make such extension of time 'as may be reasonable'. Clearly, on a major contract where delays will be very expensive both in terms of liquidated damages and the extra expense to the contractor, this kind of general wording will not be satisfactory, since it can give rise to prolonged arguments as to what is beyond the control of the contractor. It should be noted that under MW 80 no extension of time entitles the contractor to extra payment, although a variation instruction which affects regular progress will give rise to payment for loss and/or expense.

3.10 It is quite common for the provisions of the extensions of time clauses in the JCT forms to be amended, for instance by deleting the contractor's entitlement to extensions where labour and materials are not available, or where there are strikes affecting the site. There is a trap for the unwary, however. The fluctuations clauses, now printed separately from the JCT forms, state that fluctuations will continue to apply even when the contractor is in culpable delay, i.e. he has not reached practical completion by the completion date, if the terms of clause 25 (the clause dealing with extensions of time) have been amended. See, for instance, clause 38.21.2 of JCT 80. If clause 25 is amended, the appropriate fluctuations clause must also be amended.

3.11 Any delay caused by the contractor himself does not, of course, entitle him to an extension of time. This will include delays by those for whom he is responsible, e.g. his sub-contractors and suppliers. (There is an exception to this in JCT 80 in the case of nominated sub-contractors and nominated suppliers, and this is covered in more detail in para. 4.33.) The contractor is also responsible for organising the works and making sure they are properly resourced so as to achieve the date set for completion. Equally, if there is poor workmanship which causes delay because certain parts of the works have to be re-done, this also will be the contractor's responsibility. The circumstances for which an extension of time may be granted can be considered in two categories: neutral events and employer's delay.

NEUTRAL EVENTS

3.12 These are events which have not been caused by either party and where the contract provides that the contractor may be entitled to an extension of time, thereby relieving him of liability for liquidated damages but not to any further payment for losses arising out of that delay. An example of this is force majeure, discussed in more detail in para. 4.02. Other neutral events commonly referred to in an extensions of time clause are insurable perils such as fire and storm, exceptionally inclement weather and work by statutory undertakers.

EMPLOYER'S DELAY

3.13 This covers a variety of events, such as failure to give access to the site on the due date. Several of the JCT contracts now allow possession of the site to be deferred for up to six weeks, with an appropriate extension of time being granted. Where the employer or his workmen carry out work on the site at the same time as the contractor and cause the contractor delay, the contractor may be entitled to an extension of time. The most important category of employer's delays will be those arising from variations, unless (under some forms of contract) the variations are necessary in order to deal with defective work by the contractor where it may not be feasible to insist on the original construction details.

4 Typical grounds for extensions of time

4.01 In most building contracts the grounds which may entitle a contractor to an extension of time are listed in detail. Those most commonly encountered are as follows.

Force majeure

4.02 Most of the JCT forms have a comprehensive list of events which may give rise to an entitlement to extensions of time including force majeure. Since many of the incidents usually covered by this phrase, such as storm and flood, are dealt with expressly in other clauses, it is difficult to know what the phrase is intended to cover. There is no universally accepted definition of force majeure, and it must be construed in the context of the particular contract in which it appears; it may therefore mean different things in different contracts. For instance, it was held in *Matsoukis v Priestman* that the phrase included delay due to breakdown of machinery, but not bad weather, football matches or a funeral. The context of this case was unusual: the contract had been drafted by the plaintiff, a Romanian, and according to the evidence of a Belgian lawyer the phrase was understood on the European continent to mean 'causes you cannot prevent and for which you are not responsible'. It is not clear from the judgment why continental usage was relevant to an English case, except perhaps that the phrase, force majeure, originated in the Code Napoléan. It is doubtful whether breakdown of plant would ever be held to constitute force majeure in an English building contract.

Weather

'25·4·2 Exceptionally adverse weather conditions.' (JCT 80)

4.03 The government form, GC/Works/1 Edition 3, expressly excludes weather conditions as a ground for extensions of time. However, it is envisaged that where there is delay because of variations or 'the act, neglect or default of the Authority or the PM', and this delay is exacerbated by adverse weather, an extension of time will be granted which will take the adverse weather into account. In JCT 63 (no longer in print) the phrase used was 'exceptionally inclement weather'. In the later JCT forms this has been changed to 'exceptionally adverse weather conditions' which covers not only weather which is so cold, wet or windy that delays occur, but also the effects of a heatwave.

4.04 In assessing whether the contractor has been delayed for this reason, it is important to remember that the weather conditions must have been exceptional in order to give rise to a claim for delay, and that a contractor must allow in his programme for a certain amount of adverse weather which may restrict or prohibit his activities on site. If his work is programmed so that the foundations are constructed during the winter months, he will not be entitled to an extension of time merely because on some days the weather is too cold for concrete to be poured, since low temperatures are to be expected at that time of year.

4.05 As usual, the exact wording of the clause is crucial; it is the adverse weather conditions which must be exceptional and give rise to delay, not the amount of the delay suffered by the contractor.

4.06 One question which sometimes arises is whether, if within the contract period a contractor is in delay through his own fault so that, for instance, work to make the building watertight does not take place until the winter months, he can claim an extension of time for bad weather which then delays him. The argument is that, if the contractor had not already been in delay, he would have completed the watertight envelope of the building before the occurrence of the exceptionally adverse weather, which then caused him further delay. This argument has been considered by the courts and held to be invalid: delay due to the weather must be considered in relation to the work being carried out by the contractor at the time of the delay, and not by reference to the work which, according to the contractor's programme, he should have been carrying out by that date (*Walter Lawrence v Commercial Union*). Where the bad weather occurs when the contractor is in delay beyond the completion date, different rules may apply (*Balfour Beatty v Chestermount Properties*). This is discussed more fully in paras. 7.38 and 7.39.

Risks usually insured

'25·4·3 Loss or damage occasioned by any one or more of the Specified Perils.' (JCT 80)

4.07 Where delay is caused by some occurrence normally covered by the works insurance, the contractor may be entitled to an extension of time. Regardless of the insurance cover for the works, the extensions of time clause refers to 'specified perils'. The intention of the contracts is that the all risks insurance taken out by contractor or employer in the joint names of both should cover at least all the specified perils. The phrase 'all risks' does not have a clearly defined meaning in an insurance context, and the exact contingencies covered by this kind of insurance can vary from policy to policy. There may even be cases where not all the specified perils are covered by such a policy, for instance insurance against acts of terrorism. Amendment 12 to JCT 80 introduces terrorist activities as a relevant event.

4.08 Fortunately for the contract administrator, he does not have to consider the insurance position when deciding whether there has been delay because of the occurrence of a specified peril; he simply needs to look at the definition of specified perils in the contract and decide whether the event is covered by that definition. If it is, under most of the JCT forms the contract administrator must grant an extension of time (assuming all the other conditions are satisfied) even if the peril was caused by the negligence of the contractor or one of his sub-contractors. This issue was covered, albeit obliquely, in the case of *Surrey Heath v Lovell*, where the JCT With Contractor's Design form (WCD 81) had been used. In this case, a fire had caused extensive damage shortly before practical completion, allegedly due to a sub-contractor's negligence while welding in a confined space. The employer had granted an extension of time, thereby denying himself the right to claim liquidated damages for the delay in completion, and there was no suggestion that the employer had acted incorrectly by granting an extension or had been more generous to the contractor than the strict requirements of the contract.

4.09 The Court of Appeal has recently considered the meaning of the specified peril, 'the bursting or overflowing of ... pipes'. It came to the conclusion that this phrase did not cover a situation where a pipe carrying high pressure water burst after a metal purlin had accidentally been dropped on it (*Computer and Systems Engineering Plc v John Lelliott (Ilford) Ltd*).

4.10 In GC/Works/1 Edition 3 an extension can only be granted if the insured event is:

'outside the control of the contractor or any of his sub-contractors, and which could not have been reasonably contemplated under the contract.'

4.11 Thus if the event is caused by the negligence of the contractor, for instance careless welding which causes a fire on site, even if the works insurance covers the cost of reinstatement, the contractor will not be entitled to an extension of time.

4.12 The JCT Minor Works form also provides that any delay must be 'beyond the control of the contractor' to qualify for an extension of time. This would suggest that if an insured event did occur on site, the contractor would still be liable to pay liquidated damages if the works were then late in reaching practical completion. This is slightly inconsistent with the wording of the insurance clause in that form which provides that where there are existing structures and an insured event occurs, the contract administrator is to issue instructions for reinstatement which will be treated as a variation instruction so that the contractor may be entitled to any direct loss and/or expense incurred in carrying out the reinstatement.

4.13 In most of the JCT forms there is a provision whereby the contractor can obtain a quotation for the employer for insurance against loss of liquidated damages where a specified peril causes delay and an extension of time is granted. The insurance cover is usually for the same amount as the liquidated damages, and for the length of time chosen by the employer.

Strikes, civil commotion etc

'25·4·4 Civil commotion, local combination of workmen, strike or lock-out affecting any of the trades employed upon the works or any of the trades engaged in the preparation, manufacture or transportation of any of the goods or materials required for the works.' (JCT 80)

4.14 The wording of this ground for delay in the JCT forms has been criticised by the courts, because it does not state that any delay caused to the works by a strike would be covered, but refers instead to strikes 'affecting any of the trades employed upon the works or any of the trades engaged in the preparation, manufacture or transportation of any of the goods or materials required for the works'. In considering that phrasing, the court held that delay to the works caused by a strike among the employees of a statutory authority (who were also acting as the employer's direct workmen) was not covered by the terms of this clause (*Boskalis v Liverpool City Council*). The reason behind this decision is that the direct workmen were not carrying out part of 'the works', which is normally defined as the work to be carried out by the contractor. This decision is important for an employer, because delays which can be attributed to a strike or civil commotion do not entitle the contractor to extra money, whereas delays caused by the employer's direct workmen may entitle the contractor to extra payment.

4.15 The question remains, is the contractor entitled to an extension of time under this clause if a strike by one sub-contractor's workmen causes delay to another sub-contractor? It is arguable that this would fall under the terms of this clause.

4.16 The wording of GC/Works/1 Edition 3 avoids this difficulty by providing for an extension of time where there is:

> 'Any strike or industrial action which prevents or delays the execution of the works and which is outside the control of the contractor or any of his sub-contractors.'

4.17 A strike by the workmen of a statutory undertaker would fall within the terms of this clause, whether or not they were acting pursuant to statutory powers or as the employer's direct workmen because this would clearly be outside the control of the contractor. However, it can be argued that a strike by workmen of the contractor or his sub-contractors, which they could have prevented by acceding to the workmen's demands, is not outside the control of the contractor or his sub-contractors.

Instructions

> '25·4·5 Compliance with the Architect's Instructions under clauses ...' (JCT 80)

4.18 The contract administrator's power to issue instructions is governed entirely by the provisions of the building contract; he has no inherent power to issue instructions. The contract will cover, most importantly, the power to order variations to the contract works. There are also other types of instructions such as those dealing with defective work, the resolution of discrepancies between the various contract documents, postponement of the work, and, in some cases, instructions concerning sub-contractors. In general terms, where the issuing of instructions is for the benefit of the employer and does not arise out of any default of the contractor (e.g. in relation to defective work) the contractor may be entitled to an extension of time.

4.19 The work which is to be carried out by the contractor is also entirely governed by the conditions of contract, and in most of the JCT forms where the contractor is given an instruction he is entitled to know under which clause of the contract it has been given. This is important for the contractor, because extensions of time can be granted only in respect of instructions issued under certain specified clauses. It is therefore necessary for the contract administrator, when he issues an instruction, to be aware which clause of the contract entitles him to do so. Under GC/Works/1 Edition 3 this does not apply, since clause 40 allows the contract administrator to issue instructions on any matter which he considers necessary or expedient, and extensions of time are not directly related to the contract administrator's instructions.

4.20 The courts will sometimes say that a contract administrator has issued an instruction even when he has not used the usual printed form, and the word 'instruct' has never been mentioned. In *Simplex v London Borough of St Pancras* exactly this situation arose. The contractor had installed some piles which were subsequently found to be defective. There was correspondence between contractor and contract administrator on the way in which the work should be rectified. The contractor put forward proposals and asked the contract administrator for his instructions as to which remedial option should be adopted. The contract administrator, possibly not realising the implications, wrote to the contractor and said that he could go ahead on one of the proposed alternatives. This was held to be an instruction for a variation which then entitled the contractor to an extension of time.

4.21 By contrast, in a similar case, *Costain v Howard de Walden*, it was held that no instruction had been issued to the contractor. In the *Howard de Walden* case, work had been carried out by a sub-contractor which resulted in the collapse of a building façade which was to have been retained. Employer and contractor entered into a separate agreement that the necessary extra work would be carried out, without prejudice to the final decision on who was liable to pay for the reinstatement work. Since that was an agreement outside the terms of the contract, it was not held to constitute a variation, and no entitlement to an extension of time arose under the terms of the contract.

4.22 Variations can give rise to difficulties in other ways, as in the case of *Holland Hannen v WHTSO*, where progress was delayed by design defects in the work of a nominated sub-contractor. The main contractor sought an instruction to vary the sub-contractor's design so that the works could be completed, but the contract administrator was reluctant to grant this, and condemned the defective work without instructing its removal from site. The court held that the contract administrator should have issued an instruction for removal of the defective work and the design changes necessary for its completion in a satisfactory manner. This would have entitled the contractor to an extension of time and extra payment, which the employer would have to recover from the defaulting nominated sub-contractor under a direct warranty with that sub-contractor. Paras. 6.36–6.46 deal with the assessment of delay resulting from a variation.

4.23 Where a variation is instructed by the architect under clause 13A of JCT 80 (Amendment 13), the contractor will have already provided a quotation for the varied work, including his assessment of the extra time needed to carry out the work. In accepting that quotation the architect will also state the revised completion date resulting from that particular variation, and the provisions of clause 25 of JCT 80 will not therefore apply to clause 13A variations, unless they are subsequently varied without a further clause 13A instruction being issued, and where there is further delay.

Late information

'25·4·6 The contractor not having received in due time necessary instructions, drawings, details or levels from the Architect for which he specifically applied in writing provided that such application was made on a date which having regard to the Completion Date was neither unreasonably distant from nor unreasonably close to the date on which it was necessary for him to receive the same.' (JCT 80)

4.24 In this section the legal aspects of late information are considered. Paras. 6.47–6.51 deal with the assessment of any delay arising out of late information. There is an assumption with lump sum contracts that most of the design will be completed before work starts on site. However, queries inevitably arise during the course of the contract and the contractor asks for further information or details. This often happens even where the design has been largely completed by the time work starts on site. Most of the JCT forms make allowance for this, and provide that if that information is supplied late and causes the contractor delay as a result, he may be entitled to an extension of time.

4.25 An allegation of late information appears commonly in contractors' claims, and the contract administrator must consider the exact wording of the clause whenever a claim is made on this ground. The clause will apply if the contractor has not received 'in due time' some necessary information. This phrase has been considered by the courts, which held that it meant 'in reasonable time', not necessarily in time to avoid delay (*Percy Bilton v GLC*). Where it is not possible for the contract administrator to issue instructions or information in time to avoid delay because, for instance, neither party had realised sufficiently in advance that the information was necessary, the contractor may not be entitled to an extension of time under this clause.

4.26 The clause relates only to 'necessary' instructions and details. There is sometimes a grey area between information which the contractor can legitimately request from the contract administrator and the contractor's own responsibility for his method of working, with which the contract administrator cannot generally interfere.

4.27 Many contractors fail to operate this clause correctly because they do not realise that it only applies where the contractor has made a specific written application for the information. There has been some judicial consideration of what could constitute a written application by the contractor and the comments in paras. 5.01–5.14 on what constitutes a valid notice of delay are applicable here. For instance, site meeting minutes, if prepared by the contract administrator, will not satisfy the requirements of this clause since they are not a written application made by the contractor (although documents attached to the minutes, such as contractor's progress reports, could constitute a notice if they contained all the relevant information).

4.28 In *Merton v Leach* there was considerable argument whether the contractor's programme, if it set out the dates by which information was required, could constitute a notice for the purpose of this clause. It was held that it could. However, it was pointed out that if work did not proceed in accordance with the contractor's programme and there was, for instance, a delay or the contractor resequenced any of his work, the programme might no longer be a valid notice under this clause. In order to make the position absolutely clear, some bills of quantities state expressly that the contractor's programme, which is not a contract document in most cases, will not constitute notice for the purpose of this ground of delay. This is helpful, but there is a further trap in most of the JCT forms, which contain a provision that where there are bills of quantities, nothing in those documents 'shall override or modify the application or interpretation of' the JCT conditions themselves.

4.29 As to the information which the contract administrator is to provide, in *Fairweather v Wandsworth* the contractor argued that installation drawings which were to be produced by a nominated sub-contractor were the contract administrator's responsibility, and therefore if the sub-contractor was late in producing those drawings, this was a ground for an extension under the clause. (This case is discussed in more detail in paras. 7.27 and 7.28.) Since the arbitrator (from whom the case had been appealed) had held that the drawings in question were not design drawings, the judge, having accepted this, went on to state that responsibility for their production in due time was that of the contractor as part of his overall responsibility for sub-contractors' work, and delay in their production could not be laid at the door of the contract administrator. The point here was that the sub-contractors were nominated and their delay in producing drawings would arguably fall under an alternative ground for extension, i.e. delay by nominated sub-contractors which the contractor has taken all practicable steps to avoid or reduce. For the contractor, this is not such an attractive option, because an extension on that ground does not entitle him to an extra payment in relation to the delay, whereas an extension because there has been late information by the contract administrator can result in extra payment to the contractor.

4.30 There is an important proviso to the JCT clause, which is that the application must not have been made either too close to or too distant from the completion date. In *Glenlion v Guinness Trust*, considered also in para. 6.11, the contractor argued that where he had shown on his programme that he intended to complete the work early, the contract administrator was obliged to provide information at a time which would enable the contractor to maintain that programme. The court held that this was not correct. The provision of information is to be assessed in relation to the completion date, i.e. the date fixed by the contract for practical completion, not some earlier date which the contractor is hoping to achieve.

4.31 In deciding what is a reasonable period between the date of an application and the date the information is required, the nature of the works, including their size and complexity, will be relevant. If, at the outset of the works, the contract administrator specifies that a certain period should be allowed for consideration of sub-contractors' drawings, provision of extra information and the like, this will be relevant in making an assessment as to late information under the terms of this clause. It is not uncommon for contractors to submit information request sheets showing that information is required by return, or even that the date on which the information is required has already passed. The fact that a contractor has said that he requires the information by a certain date is not conclusive that there will be delay if it is not provided by that date. If information is requested by the contractor within a very short period, it could be that the contractor himself is late in requesting it, in which case it may fall outside the terms of this clause.

4.32 Looking beyond the terms of the JCT clauses to non-standard forms, in the case of *Neodox v Borough of Swinton and Pendlebury* the contract did not specify the time within which the engineer was to give his instructions and the court held that a reasonable time was to be implied, 'reasonable' being assessed not solely in terms of the convenience of the contractor, but in all the circumstances. In that case the engineer was empowered to determine the order in which the works were carried out, unlike the JCT forms, and it was held that this would affect the timing of any further instructions issued by the engineer.

Nominated sub-contractors or suppliers

> '25·4·7 Delay on the part of nominated sub-contractors or nominated suppliers which the contractor has taken all practicable steps to avoid or reduce.' (JCT 80)

4.33 This ground for an extension of time appears only in JCT 80, since it relates specifically to nominated sub-contractors or suppliers. It does not include a situation where the nominated sub-contractor or nominated supplier has ceased work altogether, e.g. through receivership or liquidation. The contractor has an obligation to avoid or reduce delay by nominated sub-contractors or suppliers, which implies at least some responsibility for supervising and coordinating their progress on the works. Following *Fairweather v Wandsworth*, discussed in para. 4.29, the contractor also has responsibility for the nominated sub-contractor's production of installation drawings. The question of responsibility for design drawings is not quite as clear. By clause 35.21 of JCT 80, the contractor is not liable for a nominated sub-contractor's design, but this does not necessarily relieve the contractor of responsibility for the nominated sub-contractor's progress in the production of design drawings. This is often covered specifically in the bills of quantities (but see the warning on bills of quantities in para. 7.01). In practice, also, there is often a close relationship between the nominated sub-contractor and the relevant design consultant in the production and appraisal of the nominated sub-contractor's design drawings.

Workmen employed direct by the employer

> '25·4·8·1 The execution of work not forming part of this contract by the employer himself or by persons employed or otherwise engaged by the employer as referred to in clause 29 or the failure to execute such works.

·8·2 The supply by the employer of materials and goods which the employer has agreed to provide for the works or the failure so to supply.' (JCT 80)

4.34 There are many reasons why it may be convenient for an employer to appoint directly some workmen who might otherwise be sub-contractors, whether a traditional form of contract or one of the management-style forms is used. The employer may have his own in-house staff to carry out aspects of the fitting-out works, for instance, or his preferred sub-contractor who has worked for him for many years and knows exactly what his requirements are. Sometimes, in the case of statutory undertakers, it is convenient that they carry out more work than is strictly covered by their statutory powers. Nevertheless, the terms under which a statutory undertaker will carry out such work are often so onerous that a main contractor is not prepared to adopt them as one of his own sub-contractors, so again it may be more convenient for the employer to engage them direct for this work.

4.35 The advantage to the employer in using direct workmen in this way is that he avoids having to pay the contractor's mark-up on his sub-contractors' prices. The disadvantage is that usually the main contractor has no responsibility for supervising their work. As far as timing is concerned, if the contractor knows that such workmen will be employed during the course of the work, he should make some allowance for this in his programme. If the contractor has no responsibility for them, however, and cannot control the progress of their work, it is reasonable that if these workmen cause delay, he should be entitled to an extension of time. In the case of statutory undertakers, it will be necessary under most of the JCT forms to assess whether any delay has arisen because of the exercise of their statutory powers or in carrying out other work for the employer, since this will affect the contractor's entitlement to extra payment.

Statutory undertakers and local authority

'25·4·11 The carrying out by a local authority or statutory undertaker of work in pursuance of its statutory obligations in relation to the works, or the failure to carry out such work.' (JCT 80)

4.36 The intention of the legislation under which privatised bodies are created to be responsible for public utilities such as water, gas and electricity, is that those bodies should be deemed to be statutory undertakers. Where either a local authority or a statutory undertaker is carrying out work under its statutory obligations, there is often a provision that if it causes the contractor delay, he will be entitled to an extension of time. Again, the contractor's programme should make some allowance for the fact that this work will have to be done, and the notice which will have to be given to the statutory undertaker as to the date on which its work is required.

4.37 It is a good idea to provide, in the preliminaries to the bills of quantities or elsewhere in the contract documents, that the contractor will make due allowance for whatever work is necessary to connect basic services, so as to avoid any doubt that the contractor has allowed for this work in his overall contract period. In the JCT contracts, for instance, this initial allowance can be made a 'provisional sum for defined work' under SMM7. The contractor also has an obligation to use his best endeavours to avoid delay, but it is preferable to obviate later disputes by making specific reference to this item in the contract documents. A claim for an extension of time on this ground would then only arise if the delay caused by the statutory undertaker or local authority was in excess of that which was reasonably included in the contractor's programme.

Government action

'25·4·9 The exercise after the base date by the UK Government of any statutory power which directly affects the execution of the works by restricting the availability or use of labour which is essential to the proper carrying out of the works or preventing the contractor from, or delaying the contractor in, securing such goods or materials or such fuel or energy as are essential to the proper carrying out of the works.' (JCT 80)

4.38 JCT 80, WCD 81 and MC 87 have a further ground for an extension where the Government exercises any statutory power which restricts essential labour or delays the contractor in securing goods, materials, fuel or energy. The clause is intended to deal with problems such as those which arose during the three-day week some years ago, and does not appear in the other JCT forms.

Lack of availability of materials and labour

'25·4·10·1 The contractor's inability for reasons beyond his control and which he could not reasonably have foreseen at the base date to secure such labour as is essential to the proper carrying out of the work; or

·10·2 the contractor's inability for reasons beyond his control and which he could not reasonably have foreseen at the base date to secure such goods or materials as are essential to the proper carrying out of the works.' (JCT 80)

4.39 In earlier forms (such as JCT 63) this was an optional clause, frequently deleted by employers. It is still optional in IFC 84, but is a standard clause in JCT 80, WCD 81 and MC 87. It is of undoubted assistance to a contractor, although it should be noted that the wording is restrictive, and relates only to labour or materials which the contractor could not reasonably have foreseen would be unavailable. In addition, the unavailable labour and materials must be 'essential' for the works. Shortage of labour and materials does not therefore automatically fall within this clause.

4.40 Deletion is essentially a commercial decision. If the clause is left in and the employer takes the risk, he may find that an extension is granted and he will lose part of his entitlement to levy liquidated damages. On the other hand, the contractor's tender price might be lower because the employer has accepted the risk.

4.41 There is a further point to note. If there are any amendments to the terms of the extensions of time clause, and any of the fluctuations clauses are used, fluctuations will continue to be updated during a period of default by the contractor after the completion date and before practical completion, whereas normally they would be frozen at the date when the contractor should have reached practical completion. If, for instance, clauses 25.4.10.1 and 25.4.10.2 of JCT 80 are to be deleted, consequential amendments should be made to the fluctuations clauses as appropriate, in order to avoid this.

Lack of access

> '25·4·12 Failure of the employer to give in due time ingress to or egress from the site of the works or any part thereof through or over any land, buildings, way or passage adjoining or connected with the site and in the possession and control of the employer, in accordance with the Contract Bills and/or the Contract Drawings, after receipt by the Architect of such notice, if any, as the contractor is required to give, or the failure of the employer to give such ingress or egress as otherwise agreed between the Architect and the contractor.' (JCT 80)

4.42 The employer will usually give possession of the whole of the site to the contractor at the commencement of the works, or possibly on a sectional basis if that has been specified in the contract. At the same time the employer must, so far as it is within his power, give the contractor access to the site in order to carry out the works, and this is usually covered by a provision in the bills of quantities or other contract document. If the employer fails to give access as stated in the contract documents, this can form the ground for an extension of time. The provision for an extension on this basis is of particular advantage to the employer, as otherwise there would clearly be a breach of contract which could give rise to all the arguments about time being at large which were discussed in paras. 2.18 and 2.19.

4.43 If, on a particular contract, the provisions regarding access are complex and the employer must, for instance, carry out prior works in order to give the contractor access, it is advisable to deal with these in as much detail as possible in the bills of quantities or other contract documents, so that the contractor is aware of the type of access which will be available. The relevant clause in the JCT forms envisages that the contractor may be required to give notice of access being required as a condition of his entitlement to an extension of time on this ground.

4.44 It is the employer's duty to give access to the site, but often the contract documents will specify that the contractor must notify the contract administrator of the dates on which particular access is required and that any adjustments to the access provisions are to be agreed between the contract administrator and the contractor.

Late possession of the site

'25·4·13 Where clause 23·1·2 is stated in the Appendix to apply, the deferment by the employer of giving possession of the site under clause 23·1·2'. (JCT 80)

4.45 At the time of tendering, a contractor will normally be informed of the anticipated date for starting work on site. This is important to him in calculating his tender sum, not only for the purpose of assessing fluctuations in the price of labour and materials, where these are to be included in the tender sum, but also for arranging for the necessary labour and materials to be available at the appropriate dates. It is quite common for the actual date for possession to be deferred during the negotiations leading up to the award of the contract and the start on site. What can sometimes happen, however, is that the anticipated start date is still inserted in the contract even though it has been superseded. Although in general it is a good idea to prepare the contract documents and have them executed before work starts on site, one of the disadvantages of doing so is that the information about matters such as the date of possession may not be entirely accurate.

4.46 For many years this issue gave great opportunity to contractors to allege that time was at large, and that the matter could not be rectified simply by adding extra time at the end of the contract, since there was no provision for the contract administrator to give an extension of time for this reason. This has now been rectified by the insertion in most of the JCT contracts of a specific provision allowing the employer to defer possession of the site for up to six weeks. If the actual start date is then delayed within that six-week period, the contract administrator can grant an extension of time. The restriction in this clause, to a six-week delay only, is for the protection of the contractor, so that he is not bound to carry out the works for the agreed contract sum subject to possibly indefinite delay by the employer. The contractor is therefore protected from the risk of being obliged to carry out the work for the same sum in a period when, for instance, he is more likely to experience bad weather which will affect the works or, if the project is delayed indefinitely, in a period when his resources have been deployed elsewhere and he cannot carry out the work as efficiently as he had anticipated.

Change in statutory requirements affecting the performance of specified work

'25·4·14 Delay which the Contractor has taken all practicable steps to avoid or reduce consequent on a change in the Statutory Requirements as to the Base Date which necessitates some alteration or modification to any Performance of Specified Work.' (JCT 80)

4.47 By Amendment 12 to JCT 80 part of the works may consist of performance-specified work, i.e. work which the contractor is required to carry out so as to meet a particular performance standard. This could apply to trussed rafters or pre-cast concrete floor units. If that work was affected by, for instance, a change in the Building Regulations or new health and safety requirements, this would not give rise to a variation, as with other kinds of work, because the performance requirement would stay the same. Nevertheless, the change in the statutory requirements might cause delay to the contractor, and this clause recognises that fact. If the contractor is delayed by a change in statutory requirements affecting performance-specified work, he may be entitled to an extension of time.

Any other act of the employer

'36(2)(e) Any other circumstances (other than weather conditions) which are outside the control of the contractor or any of his sub-contractors and which could not have been reasonably contemplated under the contract.' (GC/Works/1 Edition 3)

4.48 In some contracts, notably the Government contracts, the individual grounds for extensions of time are much abbreviated, and more general words are used. For instance, in GC/Works/2 Edition 2, the minor works form, extensions are to be granted for delay which 'has been caused or which the Authority is satisfied will be caused by any circumstance which is wholly beyond the control of the contractor'.

4.49 This general wording has given rise to some criticism by the courts. For instance, in the case of *Peak v McKinney*, a form of contract was used in which the extensions of time clause referred to various grounds for extension such as variations, strikes, force majeure 'or other unavoidable circumstances'. In that case, there was a delay of 58 weeks due to a problem with the piling, part of which was accepted as being the contractor's responsibility and part of which was held to be due to delays by the local authority, the employer under the building contract. The words 'other unavoidable circumstances' were held not to cover delay caused by the employer. One of the judges pointed out that 'if the extensions of time clause provided for a postponement of the completion date on account of delay caused by some breach or fault on the part of the employer ... the architect would extend the date for completion, and the contractor would then be liable to pay liquidated damages for delay as from the extended completion date'. It was further held that the phrase 'unavoidable circumstances' was not sufficiently specific to include the employer's breach, when read in the context of the preceding words.

4.50 The wording of GC/Works/2 Edition 2, mentioned above, is more precise. It refers to circumstances 'wholly beyond the control of the contractor' rather than 'other unavoidable circumstances'. Nevertheless, the major government form, GC/Works/1 Edition 3, has a fuller clause dealing with extensions of time, which makes a distinction between an extension for 'the act, neglect or default of the Authority or the PM' (Project Manager) and 'any other circumstances ... outside the control of the contractor ... which could not have been reasonably contemplated under the Contract'.

4.51 The decision in *Peak v McKinney* is particularly relevant in the case of extensions of time clauses which have been amended in standard forms or are contained in non-standard forms of building contract. The exact wording used is crucial.

5 Notice of delay

5.01 It is an essential part of the operation of the extensions of time clause, in most contracts, that the contractor should have given notice of delay. An exception to this is the older form, JCT 63. In *Merton v Leach*, a case dealing with this form, it was held that the contractor's obligation to give notice and the contract administrator's obligation to grant an extension were 'related but independent duties' and the contract administrator therefore had an obligation to grant an extension if the other conditions in the clause had been complied with, even if the contractor had not actually served notice of delay.

5.02 In the wording of the more recent forms, including JCT 80, the contractor's notice of delay is essential before the contract administrator is obliged to consider, prior to practical completion, whether an extension of time might be appropriate. If for some reason the contractor fails to give notice, even though he knows he is in delay, this will be a breach of contract on his part. He cannot take advantage of his own breach of contract in order to invalidate the liquidated damages clause; in any event this usually relies for its operation upon the certificate from the contract administrator that the works have not been completed by the completion date (which includes any extensions granted).

5.03 In *Merton v Leach*, the judge pointed out that there may be circumstances of which the contract administrator is aware which could lead to delay to the contract (e.g. delays caused by direct workmen), and this was part of the reason why he held that under the JCT 63 form the contract administrator had an obligation to give extensions of time if appropriate, even if the contractor had not served a notice.

5.04 Again, in JCT 80 and other recent forms, the contract administrator has an obligation to review the position on extensions of time in the period immediately after practical completion. On this review, the contract administrator can consider all relevant events, even if they have never been the subject of a notice from the contractor, and in order to do this he will need to inform himself of progress throughout the contract period. During the course of the works themselves, however, the contract administrator's obligation to consider whether an extension should be granted usually arises only if the contractor has served the appropriate notice. The exact wording of each contract must be checked to determine whether the requirements of that notice have been met. Taking, as an example, the wording of JCT 80, the contractor must give notice 'if and whenever it becomes reasonably apparent that the progress of the Works is being or is likely to be delayed'. The contractor is not therefore restricted to delays which have already occurred, but must think ahead and give notice as soon as it is 'reasonably apparent' that there is likely to be delay in the future. The obligation on the contractor is to give notice 'forthwith', and the notice must be in writing. It must set out:

(a) the material circumstances;

(b) the cause or causes of the delay;

(c) any event which in the opinion of the contractor is a relevant event, i.e. one for which the contract administrator is entitled to grant an extension of time; and

(d) details of the expected effects of the relevant events which he has identified and his estimate of the extent of the delay in completion which he anticipates, whether or not this is concurrent with delay from any other relevant event. This is to be given as part of the original notice, or as soon as possible afterwards.

Concurrency of delay, i.e. where the contractor is delayed by two or more separate events, is covered in more detail in paras. 6.52–6.61 and 7.50–7.57. In his notice, the contractor is not obliged to give an estimate of the overall delay to the works, but only the delay arising from each individual event.

5.05 The contractor is obliged to give this notice even if the delay has arisen or is likely to arise as a result of some default of the contractor himself or for some reason which does not entitle him to an extension of time. The notice must be given in relation to delay to the progress of the works even if the contractor believes that it will not ultimately affect the practical completion date. This would include, therefore, delay to the progress of part of the works which was not critical to practical completion. The contract administrator may find it helpful to have notice of this type of delay, because matters which are non-critical at this stage can become critical later.

5.06 Another type of situation can arise. The contractor's programme may show a date for completion earlier than the contractual date for completion. In the event of delay he might be prevented from completing by his own set date, but if the delay does not prevent him from completing by the contractual date, then no delay has occurred which would entitle him to an extension of time.

5.07 It is not sufficient for the contractor merely to state that he is being delayed, and the reasons for this; he must also go on to identify any of the relevant events which apply. Under the terms of JCT 80, the contractor must also give further information from time to time as is 'reasonably necessary' or as the contract administrator might reasonably require, in order to keep the information about the effects of the delay and the estimate of the amount of delay up to date. By a quirk of drafting, the contract administrator's obligation to consider and grant an extension of time is not dependent upon receipt of that further information from the contractor, but only upon the original notice and particulars of the effects etc., although he may delay in fixing the new completion date beyond the specified 12 weeks if the information he has received is insufficient.

5.08 In JCT 80 the contract administrator is given a fixed period within which to consider a notice from the contractor: either 12 weeks from receipt of the notice and 'reasonably sufficient particulars and estimate', or by the completion date if this is earlier. This last point is important. If there is an outstanding notice of delay from a contractor at the date of practical completion and the contractor has still not completed the works, he may claim that time has become at large, so that he is obliged only to complete within a reasonable time, and the employer's right to liquidated damages may also be affected. This is discussed in more detail in paras. 2.18 and 2.19.

5.09 As far as the other JCT forms are concerned, WCD 81 and MC 87 are similar to JCT 80, although in MC 87 the relevant provisions are contained in the Works Contract and incorporated by reference into the Management Contract. The wording of IFC 84, as one might expect, is less elaborate and there are some significant differences in what the contractor is obliged to provide.

The Minor Works form contains even less detail about the notice of delay, although it is still clear that the contractor must serve a notice.

5.10 In GC/Works/1 Edition 3 the contract administrator can consider an extension of time even though he has received no notice from the contractor. Under this form of contract the contractor is required to give a written progress report in advance of each site meeting (which is normally attached to the monthly site meeting minutes) describing any circumstances which have caused or may cause delay. The need for specific notice of delay under the extensions of time clause is not therefore so great. The contract administrator's time limit for granting an extension is, however, 42 days from the date of a notice from the contractor. If there is a continuing delay, e.g. a suspension of work for security reasons, the contract administrator cannot grant the total extension until the suspension has ceased to apply, but can give interim extensions as necessary.

5.11 In most standard contracts the operation of the extensions of time clause is triggered by a notice from the contractor to the contract administrator, as discussed above. This is to be a written notice from the contractor to the contract administrator. A letter to the quantity surveyor does not therefore qualify, nor does an oral report by the contractor at a site meeting, even if minuted by the contract administrator. The GC/Works/1 Edition 3 form is specific here: the notice from the contractor must request an extension of time and give the grounds for the request. The submission of a revised programme would therefore be unlikely to meet this requirement. In the case of the JCT forms, the contractor is required only to give notice of delay and appropriate details; he is not required expressly to request an extension of time.

5.12 Under most of the JCT forms the notice must state 'the material circumstances including the cause or causes of the delay'. GC/Works/1 Edition 3 requires that the contractor 'shall include the grounds for his request' in his notice, which is a similar provision. The current JCT forms also provide for the contractor to give notice of delay which he is already experiencing or which he is likely to experience in the future. This is unlike the old JCT 63 form, which was the subject of detailed scrutiny in the case of *Merton v Leach*. The findings in that case are not applicable in relation to future delay in the current forms.

5.13 As to the contents of the notice, when considering the JCT 63 form, the judge in *Merton v Leach* agreed with the arbitrator that 'the intention of the contractor's notice is simply to warn the contract administrator of the current situation regarding progress. It is then up to the contract administrator to monitor the position in order to form his opinion'. The wording of the relevant part of clause 23 in JCT 63 is that 'the contractor shall forthwith give written notice of the cause of the delay to the contract administrator'. The later versions of the JCT form go much further and, as mentioned above, require much more detail from the contractor. The 'contractor's request sheets', referred to in *Merton v Leach*, would probably not satisfy the requirements of current JCT forms as notices of delay unless they contained more than merely a warning on progress.

5.14 As to the timing of any notice, GC/Works/1 Edition 3 lays down no requirements in this respect, except that no request for extensions may be submitted after practical completion. The major JCT forms require notices to be given 'forthwith ... if and whenever it becomes reasonably apparent that the progress of the works is being or is likely to be delayed'. Although the wording in the earlier JCT 63 form is different in this respect, and the findings of the court in *Merton v Leach* are not therefore strictly applicable, it is nevertheless relevant that it was recognised that if a contractor is late in giving notice of delay, this may prevent the contract administrator from taking steps to avoid or reduce that delay. If the contractor has failed in this respect, he should not be able to benefit from his breach of contract by obtaining an extension of time greater than the extension which would have been given had the contract administrator had the opportunity to reduce delays.

5.15 Having received the required notice from the contractor and the supporting information, the contract administrator is then required to give the matter his consideration and to award an extension of time if appropriate. In reaching his decision, the contract administrator must exercise his professional judgment as to the extent, if any, that the contractor has been delayed. Although various techniques are used to determine what the contractor's delay might be, which are discussed in section 6, the assessment of delay can not be entirely scientific, and requires the exercise of the contract administrator's skill in reaching an impartial decision.

5.16 Problems have arisen in the past where a contractor has requested an extension of time but the employer, for various reasons, has not only opposed this but has attempted to influence the contract administrator's decision. In *London Borough of Hounslow v Twickenham Garden Developments* the judge said:

> 'It seems to me that an architect under a building contract has to discharge a great number of functions, both great and small, which call for the exercise of his skilled professional judgment. He must throughout retain his independence in exercising that judgment ... if an architect abdicates his somewhat special and delicate position of independence, and becomes an instrument of the building owner, then I can well see that the building owner cannot rely upon the architect's certificate.'

5.17 That case did not concern extensions of time, but the comments quoted above are equally relevant to a contract administrator's decision under the extensions of time clause. In *Perini v Commonwealth of Australia*, an extension of time was the subject of dispute. The contract administrator in that case (the Director of Works) was technically an employee of the defendants, the employers under the building contract. It was held that in assessing an extension of time he was entitled to consider departmental policy, but that he should not consider himself to be controlled by it, unless the *contractual* rights and interests of the parties required it.

5.18 Although the procedures relating to extensions of time are relatively straightforward, on a careful reading of the extensions of time clause, one or other of the parties often fails to comply with them exactly. In *Merton v Leach*, the contractor wanted to know whether the arbitrator had the power to waive a failure by the contractor to serve proper notices of delay. The court said that the arbitrator did not have such a power. This is not such an issue now, because the major forms provide for a review of extensions after practical completion, whether or not notice has been given. In that case the judge was slightly more lenient as to the contents of a notice of delay; most of the JCT forms are fairly specific as to what information is required. At the very least, the contract administrator should know whether he has received a notice of delay. A contract administrator may not always be aware that particular events or certain variation instructions are likely to cause delay, and it may be possible for him to avoid delay by omitting work or by revising his instructions if he is informed of the problem promptly.

5.19 Compared with the contractor, the contract administrator is subject to slightly less stringent requirements concerning timing. Often, he has 12 weeks (42 days for GC/Works/1 Edition 3) or, if less, the period up to practical completion in which to make his decision and, as discussed above, it is important for a contract administrator to comply with this time limit if he can. Most of the contracts give the contract administrator some discretion in this by providing that he is only required to make his decision on an extension within this time period so far as it is reasonably practicable to do so.

5.20 Having considered during the course of the contract whether to grant an extension, the contract administrator usually has a further opportunity to review his decision at the end of the contract period, i.e. within a certain period after practical completion. In those forms which do not require the contract administrator to make a decision on extensions of time unless the contractor has served notice of delay, the final review of extensions is an opportunity for the contract administrator to consider whether there have been any delays for any reason not already notified, and to grant an appropriate extension if necessary.

5.21 Even if the contractor had given no notices of delay at all, on his review the contract administrator would still have to consider whether there had been any delay for which an extension was justified. In practice this would not usually happen, as the contractor would be interested in claiming extensions as the contract progressed so that he could reprogramme his works as appropriate. For the contract administrator, the period of review is useful because by that stage he should have a clearer picture of the contract as a whole and of the factors which caused delay, although in some cases time can obscure the reasons for delay.

5.22 In making his final review of extensions the contract administrator again has a prescribed period within which to do so, usually 12 weeks after practical completion (42 days for GC/Works/1 Edition 3). In *Temloc v Errill*, a contract administrator took 19 weeks rather than the specified 12 weeks to make his final review of extensions, and the contractor claimed that this invalidated the liquidated and ascertained damages clause. The court rejected this and said that the wording of the clause: 'The Architect ... shall, if reasonably practicable ... fix such new completion date not later than 12 weeks ...', was 'directory only as to time'. The matter was considered in the context of the liquidated damages clause and not in relation to time generally nor in relation to arguments whether time had become at large. It is, nevertheless, an indication that a contractor will not usually be able to take advantage of the contract administrator's delay in making his final review of extensions. Again, this is logical, because at this stage of the contract, as long as the final review is made within a reasonable period after practical completion, there is unlikely to be any prejudice to the contractor in such a delay, since the agreement of the final account may continue for many months after the date of practical completion.

5.23 However, the time limits set out in building contracts are not always construed so generously. Everything depends on the exact wording. For instance, in *ECC Quarries v Merriman*, the ICE Conditions (Fifth Edition) were used and these set out a procedure whereby any dispute is to be referred first to the engineer for a decision. Once the engineer has given his decision, it is final and binding on both parties unless the matter is referred to arbitration within three months of the decision. There is no time limit set for the engineer to give a decision, but if he fails to do so for three months after the request, either employer or contractor may, within the next three months, require the matter to be referred to arbitration. In *ECC Quarries* the matter had not been referred to arbitration and there was a dispute over whether the engineer had given a decision. The court held that a decision had been given and that it was final and binding on both parties since there had been no reference to arbitration in the appropriate period, even though the failure to take out a reference arose in part because it was not clear whether the engineer had given a decision. This case is a useful reminder that the decisions of the courts cannot be taken for granted, and are sometimes unexpected.

5.24 To sum up, on the question of timing, the notice of delay must be served by the contractor, under most forms of contract, as soon as he is aware that there has been or is likely to be any delay. The exact wording of the clause must be consulted in each case. For the contract administrator, the contract may set out the period within which the notice is to be considered. Frequently, that period does not start until the contractor has provided sufficient details of the cause of delay and the expected length of the delay. In *ECC Quarries*, referred to above, the time limits were set out in such a way that failure to comply with them would disentitle either of the parties from referring an engineer's decision to arbitration, and this was strictly applied by the court. This is not an isolated example: in *Humber Oils Terminal v Hersent Offshore* the contractor's claim failed because he had not provided all the required information in his notice.

5.25 If there is no specific period given in which the contract administrator is to make his decision, it would have to be made within a reasonable time, which would be assessed according to the particular circumstances of the case. In the New Zealand case of *Fernbrook Trading v Taggart* the relevant English cases were reviewed, and it was held that in some circumstances, where for instance there were multiple causes of delay, it might not be possible for the contract administrator to make his final decision on extensions of time until just before the issue of the final certificate. This would only occur in an extreme case, but it illustrates the point that it can be very difficult to make a decision on extensions of time during the course of the contract itself.

6 Assessing delay

General

6.01 If the contract administrator has received a valid notice of delay, he must consider whether there has been a delay which entitles the contractor to an extension of time. This section deals with the ways in which delays to completion can be monitored and assessed, the points that should be borne in mind, and how an appropriate extension of time is awarded. 'Assessing' is used in the title because to use a word such as 'ascertain', i.e. to establish with certainty, would be misleading since in the majority of instances it is not possible to establish the exact time and length of a delay with absolute certainty. The assessment of delay involves subjective judgments, and the contract administrator must act reasonably and fairly as between employer and contractor. Throughout this section examples will be used which show an exactitude not often, if at all, found in practice, because the aim is to demonstrate the methodology and reasoning from which an assessment of delay can be derived. The word 'delay' is used rather than 'extension of time,' because a delay and its cause must be established before any consideration of an extension of time can be made.

6.02 It is important to remember that loss and/or expense or other payments of any kind are separate issues from the assessment of delay and the award of extensions of time. An award of an extension of time does not of itself create an entitlement to payment, and financial claims are mentioned only to illustrate certain points, not to indicate that there is an automatic connection with extensions of time.

6.03 In establishing whether there has been a delay to the operation or activity notified, the contract administrator must also make his own assessment of the cause of any delay; for instance, the contractor may have mismanaged the event causing the delay or he may be under-resourcing the contract. A further complication is that the contract may not require the contractor to notify the contract administrator of all delays, or the contractor may consider some events are not causing delay at all. The contract administrator should approach the task in a methodical and systematic way so that he can, if necessary, explain how he has arrived at his decision and the weight he has given to the various factors involved.

Sources of information for assessing delay

6.04 There are a number of sources of information which the contract administrator can use to monitor and assess delays:

Notices of delay.

The construction programme.

Method statement.

As-built construction programme.

Site progress meetings.

Daywork sheets and contractor's allocation sheets.

Contractor's report.

Clerk of works' reports and diaries.

NOTICES OF DELAY

6.05 Most contracts state the basic requirements of such a notice and its constituent parts. Generally speaking, the usual minimum notification requirement is to state the cause(s) and the period or estimated period of delay. If all other sources of information are absent and no accurate monitoring is taking place, such as the compilation of an as-built programme (see para 6.15), the notice of delay may be the only indication of a delay that the contract administrator receives and the only information upon which to base his decision.

THE CONSTRUCTION PROGRAMME

6.06 This is usually provided by the contractor and a contract administrator should have at least a rudimentary understanding of the principles of construction programming. The detail in any construction programme varies from project to project and usually depends upon the complexity of the project, but there are some fundamental principles that apply to any construction programme. One is that it should demonstrate how the contractor proposes to execute the works. It is both the contractor's responsibility as to how he proceeds and his right, in the absence of anything to the contrary in the contract documents, to complete the contract in any manner he sees fit. Arguably, therefore, the construction programme need not be entirely accurate. However refined the contractor's planning methods are, the construction programme is still only a subjective assessment based upon experience and judgment of how the works can be carried out. Within the construction programme, the period shown for each individual operation is only an indication of how long it is likely to take and how it interacts with other operations. It is therefore to a certain extent notional.

6.07 Most programmes will also show a critical path, i.e. the sequence of items which, if delayed, will have a delaying effect on the overall completion date. At the simplest level, any delay to items on the critical path might be expected to cause a delay to completion. There may be one critical path or there may be a number which are interrelated.

6.08 In some building contracts, the information and detail the contractor is to present in his construction programme is stated in the tender or contract documents. Sometimes the contractor's construction programme is called for before the tender is accepted so that it can be considered by the contract administrator before the contract is let.

6.09 Although the construction programme is the contractor's tool showing how he intends to progress the works, it is a useful tool for the contract administrator himself. It enables the contract administrator:

(a) to monitor the contractor's progress so as to evaluate causes of delay;

(b) to be aware when instructions and information need to be issued so as not to be the cause of a delay. (Not all contracts require the contractor to have made a written application for information before it can become the subject of a notice claiming an extension of time.)

6.10 Questions sometimes arise concerning the acceptance or approval of the contractor's construction programme by the contract administrator. Many contractors would argue that the contract administrator is not competent to question the method by which the contractor chooses to execute the works, since the contractor is the expert in this area. Given that it is the contractor's choice how he executes the works, the contract administrator's acceptance or approval of the contractor's construction programme could mean that he undertakes to provide information and issue instructions to the contractor in accordance with it. If he does not accept or approve the construction programme, but fails to provide information so that a delay results, the contract administrator is still responsible for causing delay.

6.11 Sometimes the contract administrator will indicate to the contractor that he does not think his construction programme is realistic. The case of *Glenlion Construction Ltd v Guinness Trust*, already mentioned in paras. 2.03 and 4.28, dealt with this point and the following principles were established.

- A contractor is entitled but not obliged to complete before the date for completion.
- There is no implied term that an employer has to perform the contract in such a way that the contractor can carry out the works by the construction programme completion date, if this is before the date for completion.
- The employer may not hinder the contractor in performing the contract.

If a contractor has a construction programme that shows completion at the contractual completion date and it becomes apparent that he is ahead of his own construction programme, the result of *Glenlion* is that he may effectively be slowed down by the design team, in that they are entitled to provide information in accordance with the original programme; they are not obliged to assist the contractor in achieving early completion.

6.12 If the contract documents are properly drawn up and clearly indicate when information which is not given at tender will be made available, e.g. by stating how many weeks from the contract start date it will be provided, there should be no dispute concerning the acceptability of a contractor's construction programme, since the timing for the production of information has been taken from the contract documents.

6.13 The contract administrator will use the construction programme both to monitor the contractor's progress to identify delay, and to monitor information requirements so as to prevent delay. However many revisions to the construction programme are issued, delays should always be monitored initially against the original construction programme, since revised construction programmes will reflect the delays which the contractor believes have occurred and the contract administrator may not agree with the contractor's interpretation of events. Subsequent revisions can be used to monitor how the contractor intends to complete the works and as a further check on any delays which may occur after the revisions have been issued.

METHOD STATEMENT

6.14 Sometimes the contractor submits a method statement with the construction programme. Activities within the construction programme such as piling can also have associated method statements. The same comments concerning construction programmes can be made about method statements. It can be argued that they provide an even more rigid framework within which to operate than a construction programme since they provide a detailed statement of the sequence and interrelationship of a number of activities. Because the information in the method statement is so detailed, if the contractor deviates from it and a delay occurs there will be an inference that the deviation has caused or contributed to the delay, whether or not any action of the contract administrator has influenced the delay.

AS-BUILT CONSTRUCTION PROGRAMME

6.15 The most vital source of information in monitoring progress and assessing delays is a document which records when operations and activities actually began and finished, when variations were issued and executed, when information was released and carried out. Unless there is a clear picture of how the work is actually being executed, it is virtually impossible to make any decision concerning progress or causes of delay. An as-built programme often has to be put together by both parties after completion to establish what actually happened; even then, it is difficult to establish with any certainty when any activity actually began and ended. It is essential to compile the as-built construction programme as the works progress.

SITE PROGRESS MEETINGS

6.16 These are usually concerned with progress in the broadest sense, i.e. how the work is proceeding so as to achieve the date for completion, and any action to be taken by the design team so that the contractor is not prevented from doing so. The meeting will therefore review the provision of information to the contractor, the effect of variations and the causes of delay and how these can, if possible, be overcome or mitigated. The question whether the contract administrator can accept that he has been notified of delay as a result of site meeting minutes has been discussed in para. 5.11. The contract administrator may be told in the meeting about the cause or causes of delay, which he will need to weigh against the documented evidence of delay.

DAYWORK SHEETS AND CONTRACTOR'S ALLOCATION SHEETS

6.17 Daywork sheets, where they have been used to value a variation or the contractor has presented them for 'record purposes', are an excellent means, if verified, of establishing when work was executed. The same applies to the contractor's allocation sheets, if these are made available to the contract administrator and they provide sufficient detail which can be verified.

CONTRACTOR'S REPORT

6.18 The contractor often provides a report to the contract administrator for discussion at the site progress meeting, which is usually appended to the site meeting minutes. The contract may require the contractor to notify all delays and he often does this in his report in addition to any written notification required by the contract.

CLERK OF WORKS' REPORTS AND DIARIES

6.19 Clerks of works and resident engineers often provide their own reports giving their version of delays and matters affecting progress which may or may not accord with those presented by the contractor. If both the clerk of works and the contractor perceive a delay, it is very likely that there is a delay, even though its cause and duration may be a matter of dispute and the contractor may not have given a formal notification. The clerk of works or resident engineer may also keep a diary record of events on the site which can provide a useful source of information on day to day events. Other members of the professional team may also record their observations of events on site either in diaries of their own or in the clerk of works' or resident engineer's diary. If it is the latter, the clerk of works' or resident engineer's diary can become a site diary.

6.20 The sources listed above provide a considerable body of information and records to which the contract administrator can refer to inform himself of the progress of the works and any delays, although all these will be reviewed in the light of the contract administrator's own experience.

6.21 A contract administrator's own experience may tell him if he is being given a completely distorted version of events. If an event occurs which is outside his experience, he might be wise to seek the advice of other members of the professional team or other colleagues. The look of the site, based upon his experience of other sites, may assist him in deciding whether or not there are any delays occurring or whether the whole of the works is likely to be delayed in completion. A sound knowledge of the construction process, and the relationship of design information to that process, will be required as a basis for his decisions on delay. Both the employer and the contractor, for different reasons, rely heavily on the contract administrator in this respect.

The assessment of a delay

6.22 Unless a delaying event causes delay to completion it is not relevant to the process of assessment and no extension of time need be considered. Let us suppose that there is a delay to completion. When considering any claim for delay, the contract administrator needs to be aware that awards of extensions of time should be made in calendar days and not weeks. The contract is to be performed in a calendar period, starting on one date and finishing on another, or is required to be performed in a calendar period; therefore any awards of extensions of time should be made on the same calendar basis. The period awarded should be the length of delay to the completion of the contract which is considered fair and reasonable by the contract administrator resulting from the delaying event or events in question, and should be added to the current completion date. This is often termed the dotting-on (see Glossary) or net award principle.

6.23 The standard forms of contract do not provide for an extension of time per se for trade or public holidays or, for that matter, weekends. These calendar events have to be considered in relation to the period of delay into which they fall. Further, the duration of the working day may vary from season to season. There may also be restrictions on the duration of the working week.

6.24 If the employer wishes to restrict the working day and/or working week, this must, of course, be stated in the contract. The contractor should always be asked on what working hours his tender has been based. There may also be statutory or local authority restrictions on the working day and/or week. Apart from the seasons themselves, the environment within which the works are executed may also restrict the working day and/or week and this working cycle needs to be known and understood by the contract administrator.

THE WORKING CYCLE

6.25 The effect of the cycle of a particular operation on the working day can be illustrated by an example. Suppose a bored piling operation is to be undertaken and the piling rig can complete two piles per day. Due to the nature of the operation a pile must be completed within its cycle: once bored, the pile must be concreted. If an event occurs that causes a delay for two hours, such as the rig breaking down or a variation being issued, this will affect the piling cycle and prevent a pile from being completed within the cycle. Therefore half a working day will be lost as a result of the delay event and not just two hours. This is often an important consideration where there is a restriction on working outside normal site hours, e.g. the local authority restricts all work on the site before 0800 and after 1800.

THE WORKING WEEK

6.26 The effect of the length of the working week upon an operation or activity can also be illustrated by an example. Fig. 1 shows a delay where the delaying event begins on a Monday. The contractor's working week is Monday to Friday and half-day Saturday. The working days lost by the delay are five, and this also represents five calendar days. Fig. 2 shows the same delay, but on this occasion the delaying event begins on a Thursday. Five working days are lost, but this translates into six and a half calendar days.

TRADE HOLIDAYS

6.27 The same principle would apply in considering the effect of trade holidays falling within the period of delay. Fig. 3 illustrates the position where an operation programmed for thirteen calendar days takes twenty-six and a half days to complete as a result of a delaying event. The direct effect of the delay is only five working and calendar days, but there is a consequential effect of eight and a half calendar days because of a trade holiday and a weekend.

6.28 The contractor is deemed to have allowed for the effect of trade and public holidays and weekends that occur within the contract period, but in calculating the delay caused by the event, is he entitled to this period of delay, even though it encompasses rest days which he is deemed to have taken into account? The trade holiday was probably taken into consideration within another activity which, if dependent on the first activity's completion, would be affected as in Fig. 3a. The second activity's planned duration before the delaying event was sixteen calendar days; the delay has reduced it to nine because there is no longer an intervening holiday within this activity. The overall period for the two activities before the delay event was twenty-nine calendar days; after the delay event it is thirty-five and a half calendar days, a total delay of six and a half calendar days. However, the crucial point is the effect upon the date for completion. If the second activity was the last activity before contract completion, then the effect upon completion would be the total six and a half calendar days.

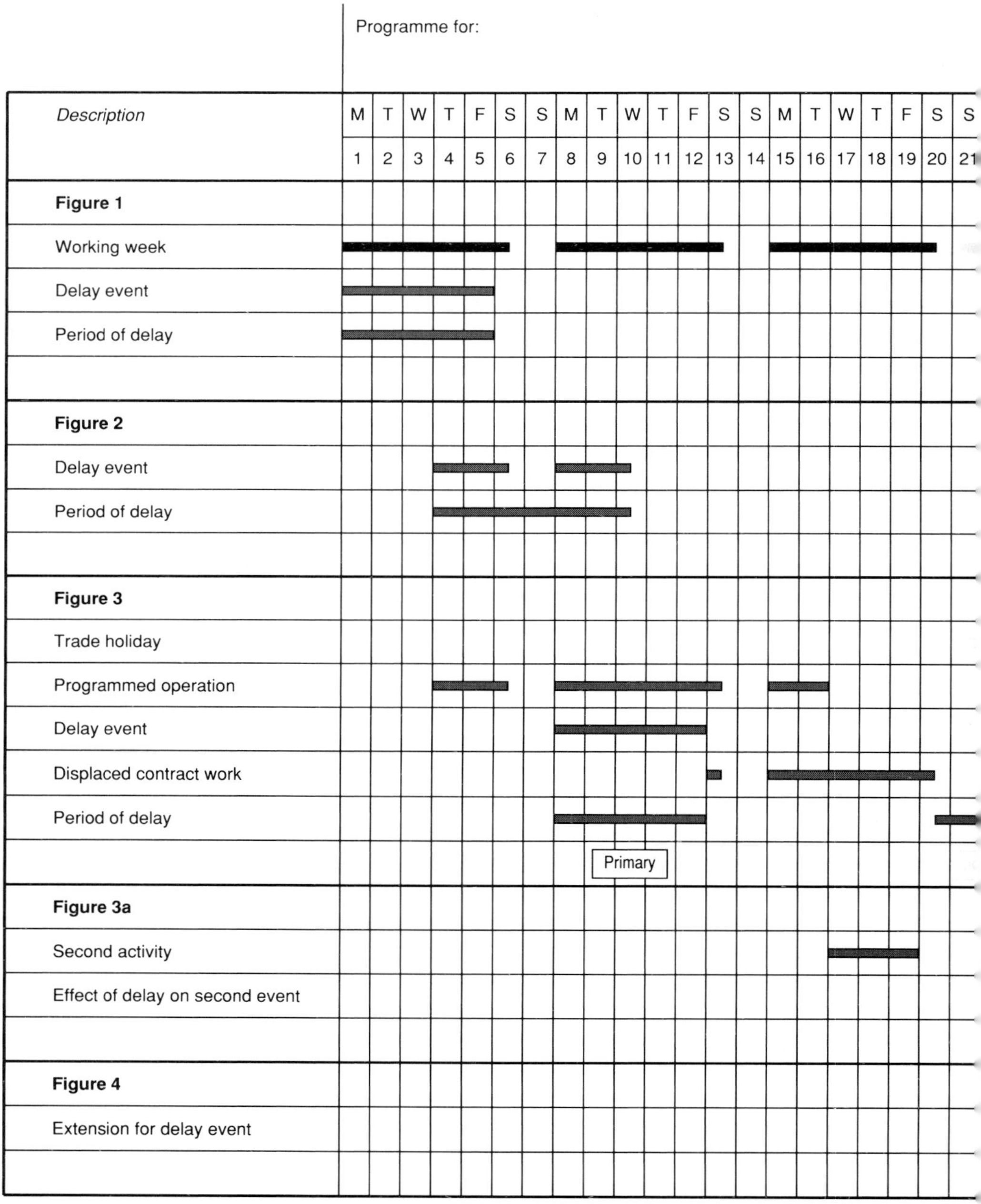

Programme for:

Description	M	T	W	T	F	S	S	M	T	W	T	F	S	S	M	T	W	T	F	S	S
	1	2	3	4	5	6	7	8	9	10	11	12	13	14	15	16	17	18	19	20	21
Figure 1																					
Working week																					
Delay event																					
Period of delay																					
Figure 2																					
Delay event																					
Period of delay																					
Figure 3																					
Trade holiday																					
Programmed operation																					
Delay event																					
Displaced contract work																					
Period of delay																					
										Primary											
Figure 3a																					
Second activity																					
Effect of delay on second event																					
Figure 4																					
Extension for delay event																					

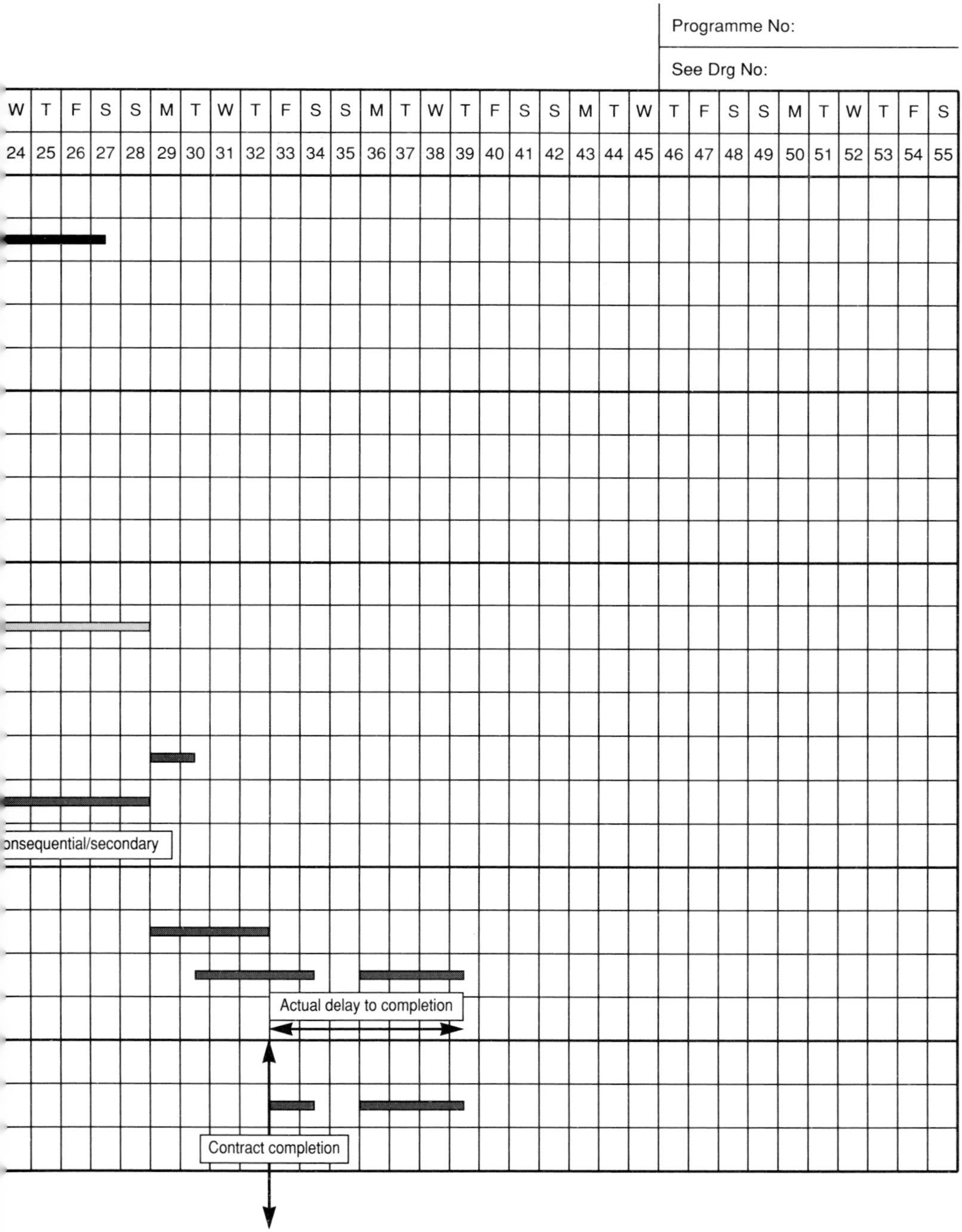

Programme No:

See Drg No:

W	T	F	S	S	M	T	W	T	F	S	S	M	T	W	T	F	S	S	M	T	W	T	F	S	S	M	T	W	T	F	S
24	25	26	27	28	29	30	31	32	33	34	35	36	37	38	39	40	41	42	43	44	45	46	47	48	49	50	51	52	53	54	55

onsequential/secondary

Actual delay to completion

Contract completion

6.29 In considering the effect of this delay event, the contract administrator could adopt one of two approaches. He could take the view that the event caused a delay of five working days and add these to the end of the contract period, as in Fig. 4. The five working days become six and a half calendar days because the contractor is not deemed to have allowed for weekends and trade holidays that occur outside the contract period. If, however, the week following the date for completion was a trade holiday, as in Fig. 5, the effect would be thirteen and a half calendar days. Alternatively, if the contract programme is sufficiently detailed and considered reasonably accurate, the contract administrator could follow the effect of the event through the critical path and establish the effect of the delay. Given the fact that the effect on the date for completion is six and a half calendar days in Figs. 3 and 3a, does it matter? It does, because there has been a change in the calendar periods within which the two activities are being executed as a result of the delay event. The first activity has changed from thirteen calendar days to twenty-six and a half calendar days, and the second activity has changed from sixteen calendar days. These changes may have an effect on later events.

6.30 If an extension of time has been awarded and, when the contract has been extended by the duration of the award, the extended date falls within a trade holiday as in Figs. 4 and 5, the date for completion must be extended beyond the trade holiday, a further calendar week. The contract, as already stated, does not allow for extensions of time for trade holidays, so why is the trade holiday included in the extension of time? Because, on the same principle as applied to Fig. 3a, a consequential effect of the event is to extend the contract into the holiday period; it should therefore be included in the event for which the extension to the contract period was made.

6.31 One of the problems of the consequential effect of delay is that some previous delay may have been caused by the contractor. For example, in Fig. 4, if the extension had not been given because the delay was the contractor's responsibility, this would have delayed completion into the period of the trade holiday, a consequential effect of the contractor's own delay.

6.32 It is suggested that it is not possible to fix a completion date within the period of a trade holiday and it must therefore be placed beyond the trade holiday. However, when the question of loss and/or expense arises the contract administrator must consider which party is responsible for the fact that the delay has extended into and beyond a trade holiday.

CONSEQUENTIAL EFFECT OF THE SEASONS

6.33 A further consequential effect of a delay event may result from the seasons, for instance where a contract is intended to end at the end of the summer and delays during the original contract period push the contract into the winter. The contractor may have programmed for weather-sensitive work to be carried out in the summer and this work must now be carried out in the winter. If further delays occur as a result of the winter which are not necessarily weather conditions that would give rise to an extension (e.g. exceptionally adverse weather under JCT 80) but merely those that affect progress, these delays will be a consequential effect of the previous delay. The contractor should only receive an extension of time for these consequential delays if he has been awarded an extension of time which places the revised completion date within the adverse season. This may be further restricted in view of the sequence of the delays that have occurred. The contract administrator should consider whether delays caused by the contractor prior to the delay for which he is to receive the extension of time have moved the contractor's work into this season rather than the extension of time event. If this is the case the contract administrator should bear this in mind when assessing the actual cause of delay.

THE SEASONS WITHIN THE CONTRACT PERIOD

6.34 The contractor is deemed to have allowed for the effect of weekends and holidays within the original contract period. Similarly, he is deemed to have allowed for the effect of the seasons and the times they occur within the original contract period, except for weather conditions which are so severe that they give rise to an extension of time. If a contractor has, say, a summer – winter – summer contract period, his programme of operations may be geared to that cycle. If delay breaks that cycle through no fault of his own and he receives extensions of time, he is also entitled to an extension of time for the consequential effects of that delay in putting work back into the 'wrong' season, if this causes further delay.

IDENTIFYING THE DELAY ITSELF

6.35 The occurrence of some events, such as strikes and adverse weather, can be identified relatively easily. The contract administrator is generally aware of when they occur, and provided that records are kept of when the strike or adverse weather began and ended, the period of the primary (direct) delay can be assessed. The only other factor to consider in establishing the period of the delay is the consequential effect of the event, as discussed above.

6.36 A delay caused by a variation involving the addition, omission or substitution of any work, which may also include the alteration of the kind or standard of materials or goods used, is more complex. It is important, first, to identify when the variation was executed. Ideally, a variation instruction should be issued timeously, i.e. in sufficient time for it to be included within the operation that it affects. Thus its effect is only to increase the time taken to execute that operation as if the instruction had been included in the original contract works and the contractor could have programmed and organised the work accordingly, irrespective of the contract period.

6.37 Additional or substituted work does not necessarily cause a delay, nor is the value of the work involved in the variation an indicator of a delay: it is the material and physical content that is relevant. For example, the substitution of gold-plated taps for chromium-plated steel taps will probably increase the value of the work, but it may make no difference to the time taken to execute it.

ADDITIONAL WORK – ADDITIONAL LABOUR?

6.38 Additional work to an operation or activity is always likely to increase the time taken to carry out that activity and hence delay its completion in the absence of 'accelerative' measures such as additional resources or overtime working. Substituting gold-plated taps for chromium-plated ones should not delay the completion of fixing the number of taps in the contract, but if the number of units having taps is increased from ten to twenty, whether they have chromium-plated or gold-plated taps, there is more likely to be a delay in the completion of the operation.

6.39 In this kind of situation contract administrators sometimes argue that the contractor should increase his resources. The argument runs like this: the contractor has been paid for the additional ten taps, therefore he can employ additional plumbers to fix the additional taps at the same time as the original taps. There is some contractual basis for this argument. For instance, JCT 80 in clause 25.3.4.2 states: 'the contractor shall do all that may be reasonably required to the satisfaction of the contract administrator to proceed with the works'. Clause 25.3.4.1 also provides: 'the contractor shall use constantly his best endeavours to prevent delay in the progress of the works, howsoever caused, and to prevent the completion of the works being delayed beyond the completion date'. The concept of best endeavours is discussed in para. 7.61 onwards.

6.40 Nevertheless that argument very often does not apply. Labour is not an entirely flexible resource. Irrespective of the labour market, it is not usually possible to increase (or decrease, since the additional plumbers will only be required for a short time) the labour resources on a site at will, especially for work which was unforeseen and of possibly intermittent and short duration, for the same price as the original tendered work. The contract usually envisages the proper evaluation of varied work in respect of:

(a) work not executed under similar conditions;

(b) significant changes in quantity;

(c) work not of a similar character.

However, it does not envisage the valuation of additional resources in order to execute the increased amount of work in the same period unless this has been instructed. This would effectively be an instruction to accelerate which is not provided for in most of the standard forms.

6.41 Even if additional labour resources are obtainable, they may cost more than the contractor will be recompensed for the variation, particularly where the varied work is small and of short duration in relation to the additional resources. Clearly, the contractor should organise his existing labour resources so as to carry out the varied work as efficiently as possible. This may involve reorganising his work gangs and/or re-programming his work, but the use of

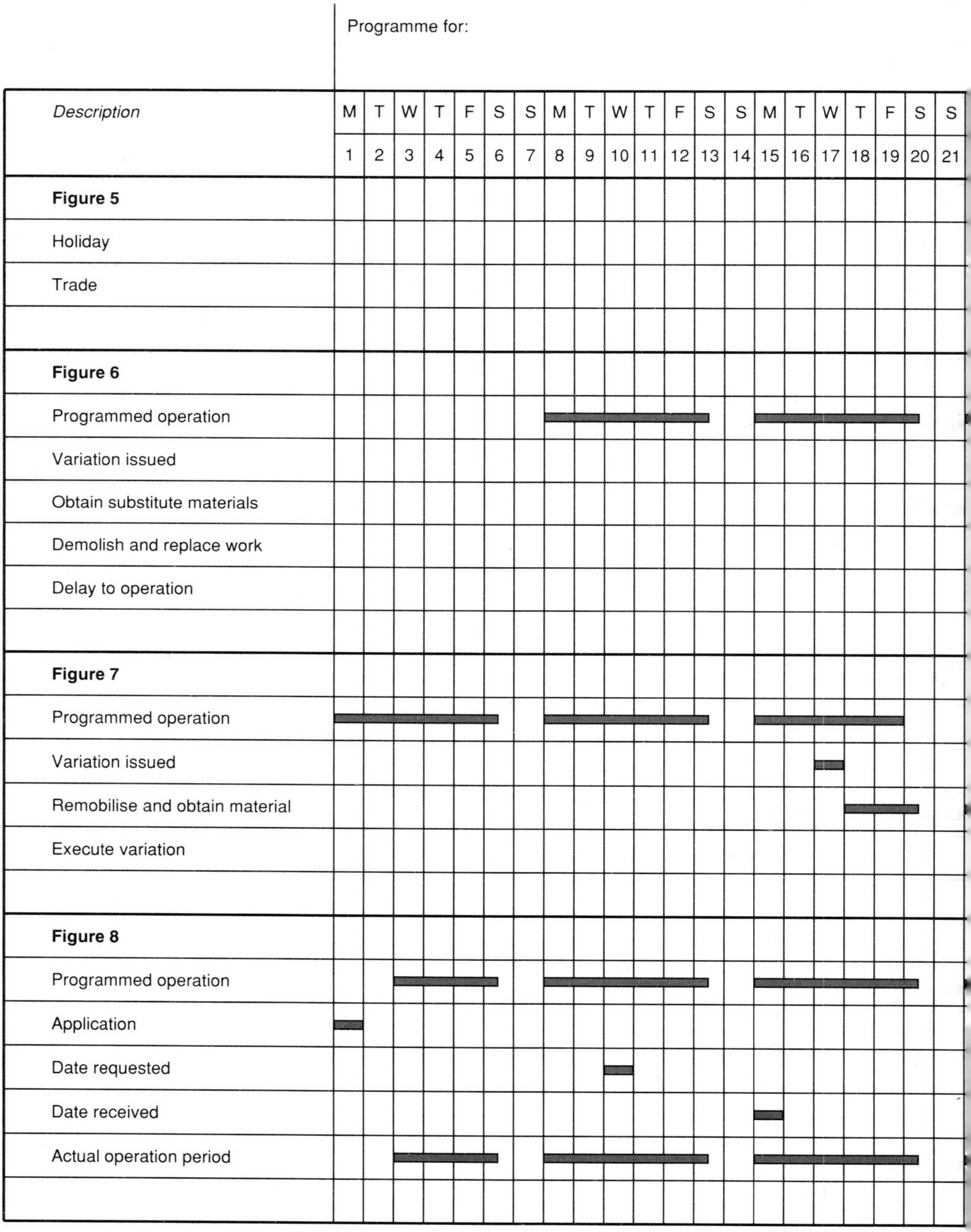

Programme for:

Description	M	T	W	T	F	S	S	M	T	W	T	F	S	S	M	T	W	T	F	S	S
	1	2	3	4	5	6	7	8	9	10	11	12	13	14	15	16	17	18	19	20	21
Figure 5																					
Holiday																					
Trade																					
Figure 6																					
Programmed operation																					
Variation issued																					
Obtain substitute materials																					
Demolish and replace work																					
Delay to operation																					
Figure 7																					
Programmed operation																					
Variation issued																					
Remobilise and obtain material																					
Execute variation																					
Figure 8																					
Programmed operation																					
Application																					
Date requested																					
Date received																					
Actual operation period																					

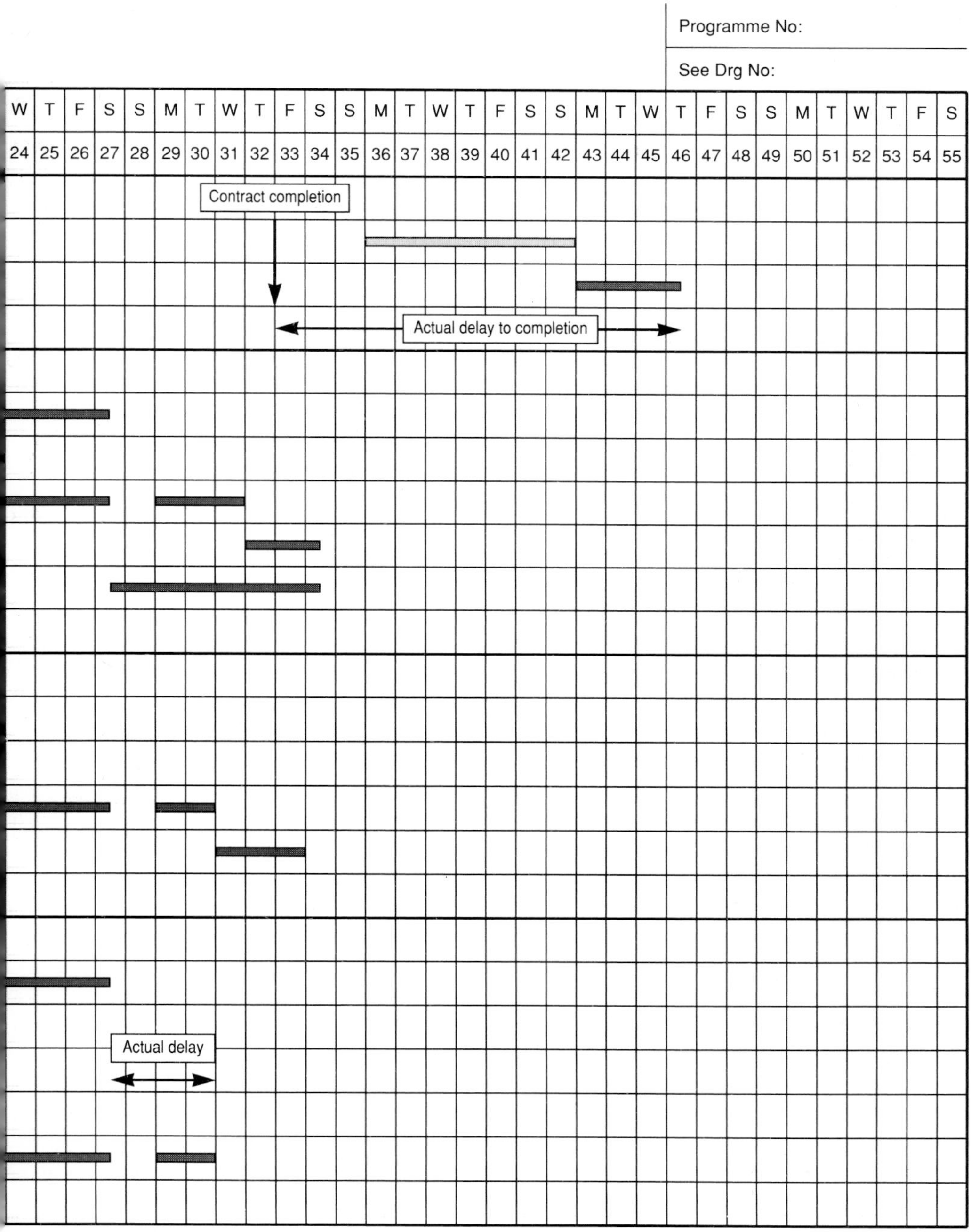

Programme No:

See Drg No:

W	T	F	S	S	M	T	W	T	F	S	S	M	T	W	T	F	S	S	M	T	W	T	F	S	S	M	T	W	T	F	S
24	25	26	27	28	29	30	31	32	33	34	35	36	37	38	39	40	41	42	43	44	45	46	47	48	49	50	51	52	53	54	55

Contract completion

Actual delay to completion

Actual delay

additional labour resources will be unlikely unless the cost can be fully recouped under the contract.

TIME TAKEN TO EXECUTE VARIED WORK

6.42 The contract administrator, in assessing what is a 'fair and reasonable' delay, must calculate the time it would take to do the varied work, on the assumption that the contractor is properly resourced and managing the contract efficiently.

6.43 Returning to the example of the taps, if this item appears on the contractor's programme as a separate activity, there are three possible outcomes:

(a) the additional work will take twice as long as the original programmed period (there is twice the amount of work) subject to any weekends or statutory holidays; or

(b) the additional work will take longer than twice the programmed time; or

(c) the additional work will take less than twice the programmed time.

It is assumed that the contractor has given notice of delay before the extra work has been done. For outcome (a) to be the 'fair and reasonable' delay, the following at least would have to apply:

(1) the original programmed period must have been correct for the current level of resources;

(2) the contractor must be using the correct level of resources;

(3) the contractor must be correctly managing the works.

In the case of (b):

(1) the original programmed period was not correct for whatever reason; and/or

(2) the contractor is using the correct level of resources but the original programmed period was not correct; and/or

(3) the contractor is not employing the correct level of resources; and/or

(4) the contractor is mismanaging the works.

In the case of (c):

(1) the original programmed period is not correct for whatever reason; and/or

(2) the contractor is using the required level of resources but the original programme period is not correct; and/or

(3) the contractor has reorganised his works so that less time is lost.

The question whether the contract administrator can wait for the delay actually to occur before dealing with the claim for an extension of time was discussed in paras 5.03 and 5.04. Even if he does wait, one of the three outcomes will still happen. The contract administrator must decide what would be a fair and reasonable delay caused by the variation in the circumstances.

6.44 If the necessary materials and labour are not immediately available to carry out the variation and this contributes to the delay, then some consideration must be given to this aspect of the delay, since it is a direct result of the variation itself and not a general inability to secure labour and materials for the original contracted work.

LATE VARIATIONS

6.45 In addition to the factors already considered, there may be further delay if the issue of the variation is not timeous. In the case of substituted work, this could mean that work which has already been constructed has to be taken down and replaced, or materials already purchased have to be returned if possible and the substituted materials ordered. In the case of additional work, it could result in the remobilisation of labour and plant for an operation previously completed, and a delay in ordering materials. The most important point to consider is: when could the work reasonably have been carried out? Fig. 6 gives an example of a delay to an activity caused by a late variation which substitutes work. A late variation for additional work could have the same effect, and where the operation has already been demobilised it could put such a delay into a time period of its own. In Fig. 7, the period needed to execute the work is three calendar days. It could be argued that this is the only period that should be considered for an extension of time. However, if the date shown on Fig. 7 was the earliest possible time this work could have been executed following receipt of the variation instruction, due to remobilising and obtaining materials, the delay to the operation is 14 calendar days.

6.46 The omission of work, if instructed timeously, effectively reduces the time to complete an activity. The same principles as those which apply to additional work are relevant.

LATE INFORMATION

6.47 This ground for claiming an extension is a favourite with contractors, and the one which causes most difficulty, because it potentially constitutes a direct criticism of the contract administrator himself. It is therefore important to deal with such claims carefully and impartially. It is necessary to distinguish between late information, such as drawings and specification details, which will be termed design information for the present purpose, and 'late' instructions requiring a variation to the works, such as modified or additional work, as discussed above. The expression late information is often used without clearly defining what is meant by it. Design information may be described as 'late' because it has been issued later than programmed, but this may only be technically late. It cannot be emphasised too strongly that design information is only late in the context of claims for extensions of time if it causes a delay to the completion date (see paras. 4.22–4.30).

6.48 JCT 80 allows an extension of time for late design information 'for which he (the contractor) specifically applied in writing provided that such application was made on a date which having regard to the completion date was neither unreasonably distant from nor unreasonably close to the date on which it was necessary for him to receive the same' (clause 25.4.6.). For the purposes of this discussion it is assumed that this precondition has been met. The completion date referred to in the clause is 'the date for completion as fixed and stated in the appendix or any date fixed under either Clause 25 or 33.1.3'. It should be noted that the proviso to clause 25.4.6 is to the application itself and not to the provision of the information.

6.49 The argument that usually arises is whether:

(a) the contractor is entitled to receive information at a time which relates to the completion date, even if it is apparent that he will not complete by that date. If the contract administrator fails to provide the information, he denies the contractor the opportunity to 'catch up', and the contract administrator is then condoning the delay; or

(b) the contractor is entitled to receive information according to his progress.

The crucial point is that the information is only late if it gives rise to a delay to completion. Thus, design information should be provided in sufficient time for the operation or activity to progress in relation to its current completion date. Any design information not provided in accordance with this principle and which causes a delay is late.

6.50 Fig. 8 shows a delay resulting from late design information. It is sometimes argued that the period of 'delay' is the time from which the contractor ought to have received the information to the time when he did receive it, five calendar days in Fig. 8, but this presupposes that the information is vital to progress and that the lack of design information effectively suspends progress until it is received. The design information is only late in respect of an extension of time if it gives rise to a delay to completion of the contract. Design information is rarely so vital that it causes an absolute suspension of an activity, although it might halt a sub-activity; it may be that the contractor finds it more efficient to suspend the activity until all the information is available. In Fig. 8 the actual delay to the operation is shown as three and a half calendar days. If there are no other delaying factors, this will be the delay caused by the late information. If the activity or operation shown in Fig. 8 had ended on the date originally programmed, no delay would have resulted, even though the information had been provided late.

6.51 Fig. 9 shows the situation where a 'delay' occurs when a

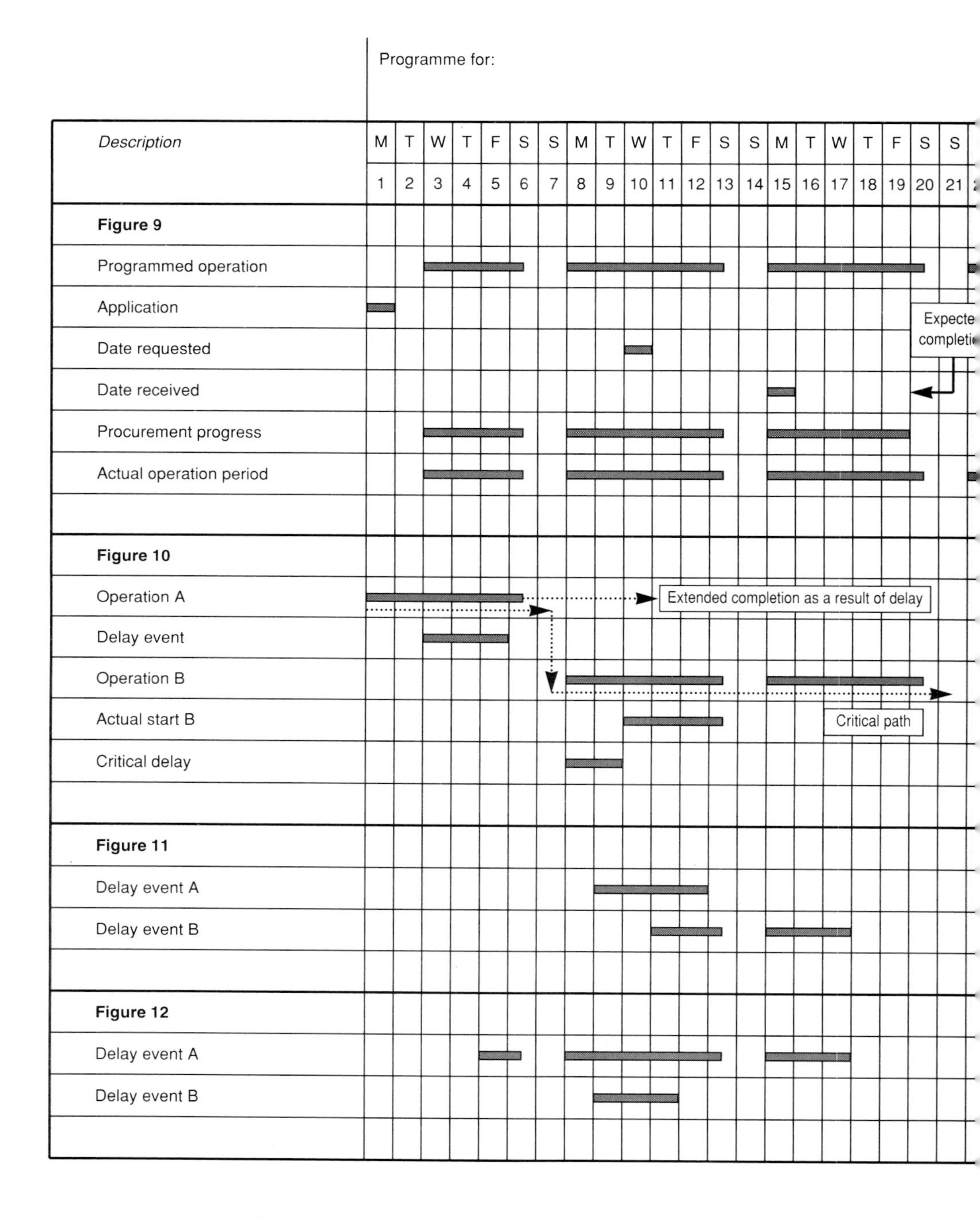

Programme for:
Description
M T W T F S S M T W T F S S M T W T F S S
1 2 3 4 5 6 7 8 9 10 11 12 13 14 15 16 17 18 19 20 21
Figure 9
Programmed operation
Application
Date requested
Date received
Procurement progress
Actual operation period
Figure 10
Operation A
Extended completion as a result of delay
Delay event
Operation B
Actual start B
Critical path
Critical delay
Figure 11
Delay event A
Delay event B
Figure 12
Delay event A
Delay event B

Programme No:

See Drg No:

W	T	F	S	S	M	T	W	T	F	S	S	M	T	W	T	F	S	S	M	T	W	T	F	S	S	M	T	W	T	F	S
24	25	26	27	28	29	30	31	32	33	34	35	36	37	38	39	40	41	42	43	44	45	46	47	48	49	50	51	52	53	54	55

programmed operation is expected to complete earlier than programmed but 'late' information causes a 'delay'. Is there a delay? An extension of time should only be awarded if the information delay caused a delay to completion; in practice, this would mean following through the event shown in Fig. 9 to see its effect upon the date for completion. Information delays are not easy to assess because the effect of late information is often the most difficult to identify accurately.

THE CONCEPT OF CONCURRENT DELAYS

6.52 (See also paras. 7.50–7.57.) While considering the cause of delay to completion of the contract, the contract administrator may find there is more than one cause occurring at the same time. This is referred to as concurrent delay. It is interesting that most, if not all, of the standard forms of building contract assume that delays follow each other in clear succession, and do not recognise the possibility of concurrency.

6.53 It is very rare for absolute concurrency to occur; there is usually an overlap. Fig. 11 illustrates this. It should be understood that concurrent delay only exists when two identifiable delays, both of which affect completion, occur at the same time. Concurrent delay does not necessarily arise when the contractor is in culpable delay, having failed to finish by the completion date when a delaying event occurs, because the work he is executing at that time is work that has been displaced by previous delays. The contractor is in delay during that period but he is not necessarily carrying out the works more slowly than he should.

6.54 The concurrency of delays is only important where both events are critical to completion. If one of the events is not critical and the other is, the delays may be concurrent but in terms of delay to completion there is no concurrency. Where both events are critical to completion because they are on separate critical paths, or there are delays on sub-activities of a critical activity, the delays are concurrent. This raises two issues. First, if two events occur at the same time, both of which entitle the contractor to an extension of time, should one, or both of them, or part of each, form the reason for the extension of time? Secondly, if two events occur at the same time which cause a delay to completion, one being the responsibility of the contractor and the other entitling the contractor to an extension of time, should an extension of time be awarded and, if so, of what duration? There may, of course, be more than two events involved.

6.55 In Fig. 11, if delay event A and delay event B are both events which would entitle the contractor to an extension of time and affect different operations on site, the delay caused to operation X by event A is four calendar days, and the delay caused to operation Y by event B is seven calendar days. The overall delay is nine calendar days. To keep the example simple, it is assumed that the delay carries forward through the critical path(s) to show an effective delay to completion of nine calendar days. As both events give rise to an extension of time to the contractor, does it matter? Can the contract administrator simply award the nine calendar days? JCT 80 requires, as does GC/Works/1 Edition 3, that the contract administrator should state the cause(s) of delay. In the absence of a contractual requirement it would be good practice to state the reasons for the award.

6.56 The most difficult problems with concurrent delays occur where (referring to Fig. 11) delay event A is the responsibility of the contractor and delay event B is one for which the employer has taken the risk, since it entitles the contractor to an extension of time. Is the contractor entitled to an extension of time and, if so, for what period? There are three alternatives.

(1) Delay A, the contractor's delay, because it starts first must run its course before delay B delays the contract, and therefore the extension of time would be five calendar days. If the employer's delay was A and the contractor's B, then, by the same logic, the contractor would receive an extension of time of four calendar days.

(2) Although delay A, the contractor's delay, begins first, if this delay were given primacy for the two calendar days during which there are events which are the employer's risk, the employer would be entitled to levy liquidated damages for a period where delay was occurring which was his risk, which is not 'fair and reasonable' and possibly could be construed as a penalty; therefore, the contractor is entitled to a seven-day extension of time. This argument would not apply if the employer's delay was delay A. The extension of time would in that case remain at four calendar days.

(3) The contractor and the employer take responsibility for the delays wholly at their respective risks, and the two days' delay for which they are both responsible is divided between them, thus the extension of time for the contractor is six days.

6.57 The third alternative attracts the same criticism as the first: that the employer is entitled to liquidated damages for a delay which is partly at his risk. If the two delays began together and ran for exactly the same period, would the logic of the third alternative be acceptable? Would it be logical and reasonable to split the delay between the two parties? If the two delays began together but the employer's delay ran beyond the contractor's delay, would the contractor receive the whole period as an extension of time? Or, if the two delays began together but the contractor's delay ran beyond the employer's delay, does the contractor receive an extension of time? There is no clear answer to these questions and the courts have given only limited guidance. It is arguable that, to be fair and reasonable, the contract administrator should give an extension of time for all delays to completion which are at the employer's risk and covered by the extensions of time clause.

THE DOMINANT DELAY APPROACH TO CONCURRENT DELAY

6.58 Dominant delay is an approach to concurrent delay in which the overriding cause of delay predominates in the assessment of delay. Fig. 12 is an example of this. It should be understood that both delays must affect completion; the theory does not apply where one of the delays does not affect completion and is not critical and the other delay does affect completion. Delay event A is regarded as dominant as it encompasses the delay caused by event B so that, in effect, event B does not make any difference to completion.

6.59 Fig. 13 is another example of dominant delay, in relation to two critical operations: pile heads and ground beams, and the structural steel frame. The contractor is responsible for designing the steelwork connections. The contract administrator issues an instruction for a variation to the ground beams, which causes a four calendar day delay to that operation. At the same time, the contractor is in delay in designing the steelwork connections so that the steelwork cannot start at the programmed time. This causes a fourteen calendar day delay to the start of this work from the original programmed start, and is also ten days later than the date the work could have started even allowing for the variation delay. Because of the dominance of the contractor's delay, the variation delay has no effect upon the completion date.

6.60 The argument is entirely dependent upon the criticality of both operations to completion. Take another example, Fig. 14, where the next critical operation after the ground beams is drainage and the steelwork does not come on to the critical path until the drainage is completed. Then, when a week's work has been completed on the steelwork, the ground floor slab comes on to the critical path. As Fig. 14 shows, if, although the contractor's delay is the greater, it is not critical to completion, the cause of delay is the variation.

6.61 Dominant delay can only apply where:

- both delay events are critical to completion; and
- the dominant delay event clearly starts before and ends after the other delay event or events; and
- the dominant delay event is a continuous unbroken delay event.

See para. 7.50 onwards for further discussion of this concept.

CONTINUAL DEFAULT

6.62 Where either the contract administrator or the contractor is involved in a continuing default there can be concurrent delay which has the characteristics of dominant delay but which occurs over a period, sometimes the whole of the contract, and causes a steady loss of time. The accusation made by the contract administrator concerns three broad areas:

- poor management;
- under-resourcing of labour; and
- poor workmanship.

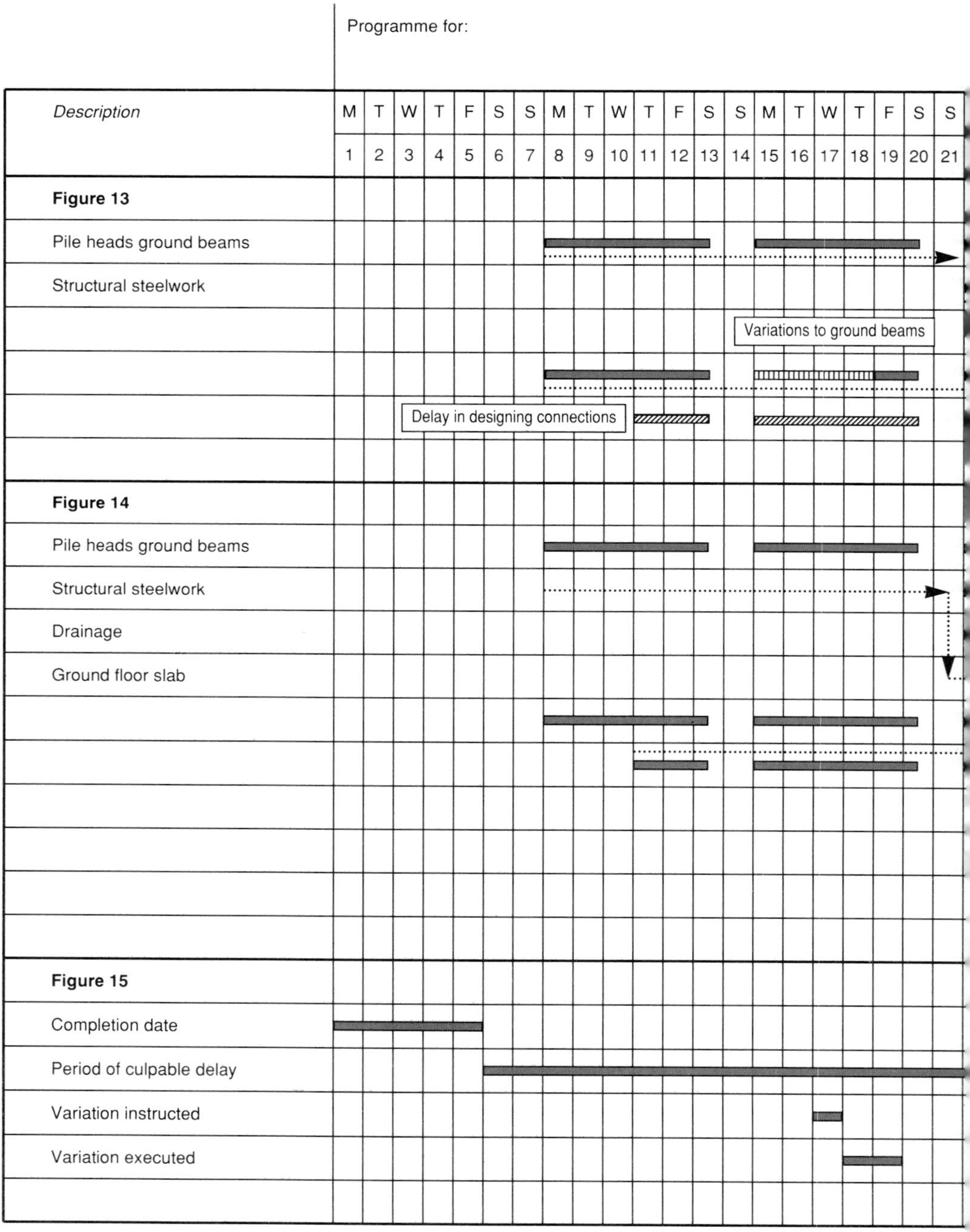

Programme for:

Description	M	T	W	T	F	S	S	M	T	W	T	F	S	S	M	T	W	T	F	S	S
	1	2	3	4	5	6	7	8	9	10	11	12	13	14	15	16	17	18	19	20	21
Figure 13																					
Pile heads ground beams																					
Structural steelwork																					
															Variations to ground beams						
			Delay in designing connections																		
Figure 14																					
Pile heads ground beams																					
Structural steelwork																					
Drainage																					
Ground floor slab																					
Figure 15																					
Completion date																					
Period of culpable delay																					
Variation instructed																					
Variation executed																					

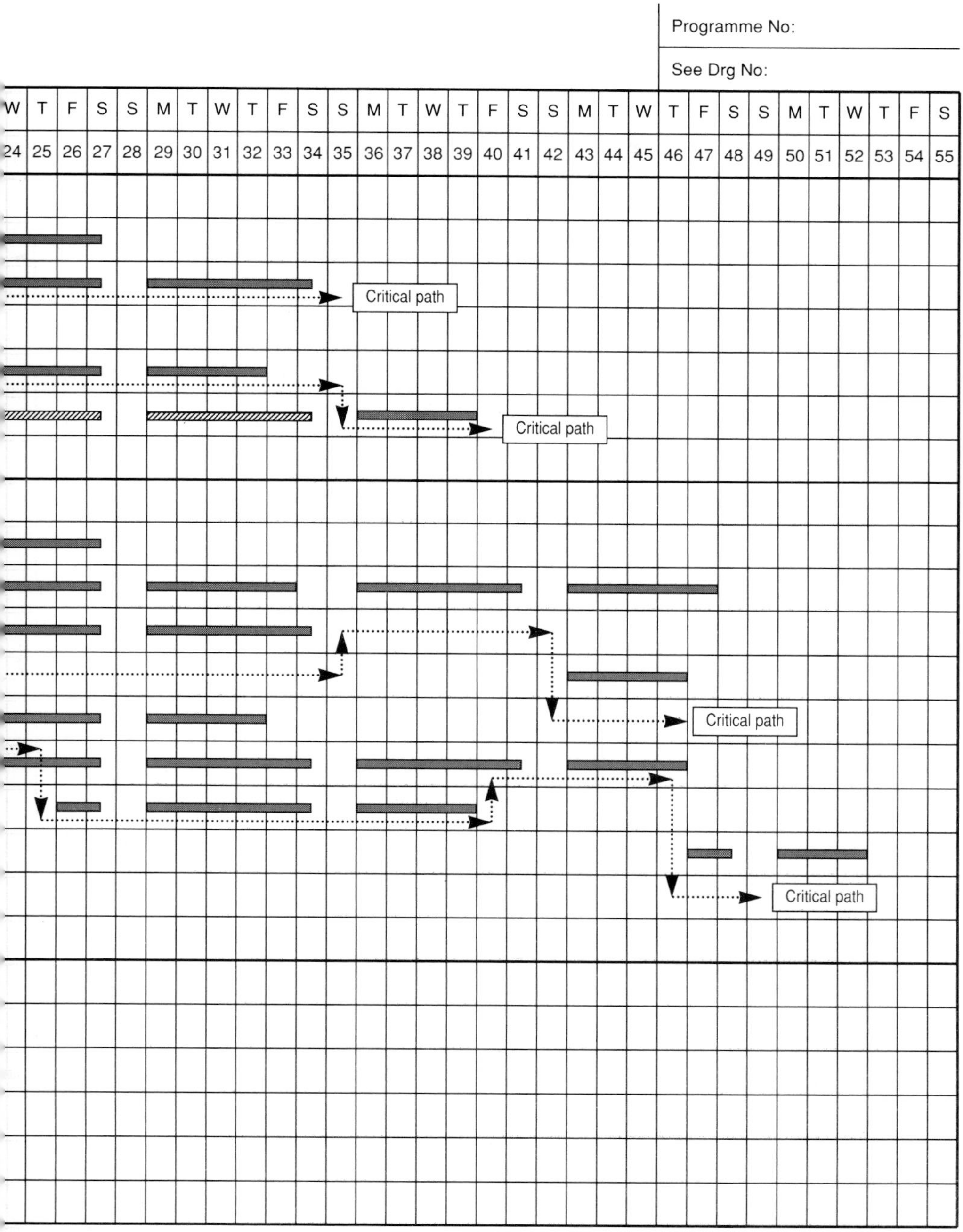

Programme No:

See Drg No:

W	T	F	S	S	M	T	W	T	F	S	S	M	T	W	T	F	S	S	M	T	W	T	F	S	S	M	T	W	T	F	S
24	25	26	27	28	29	30	31	32	33	34	35	36	37	38	39	40	41	42	43	44	45	46	47	48	49	50	51	52	53	54	55

Critical path

Critical path

Critical path

Critical path

6.63 In the absence of any other delaying events, such defaults on the part of the contractor would be evidenced by a continuing increase in delay to completion. However, when the contract administrator issues variations or provides design information late and other delay events occur, the cause of delay can become obscured. There is an argument that because the contractor is in continual default he is not entitled to an extension of time, even for events for which he would ordinarily be entitled to one. However, this argument cannot be valid; if it were, the contract administrator could continually issue variations and provide information late for the critical activities with impunity, causing the date for completion to be delayed even further. Each variation will, of course, take longer to execute because of the under-resourcing, but the contractor is still entitled to a fair and reasonable extension of time for those delaying events which are at the employer's risk. That extension of time should, of course, reflect the situation if the contractor had not been in default. For example, in a situation of under-resourcing of labour where a variation is issued, the contractor would only be entitled to the extra time it would have taken if he had been properly resourced. It could be argued that this defeats the logic of dominant delay, but this is not necessarily the case. Dominant delay relies upon the existence of two clearly identifiable unbroken delay periods. The continual defaults described can only be identified as a particular loss of time over a period of time. For example, as a result of being under-resourced with labour, the contractor loses half a day a week in productivity. Although described as continual, this default is in fact intermittent in its effect.

6.64 Difficult problems arise where continual default is claimed by both the contractor and the contract administrator against each other. The contractor is accused by the contract administrator of being continually under-resourced and mismanaging the works and continually slipping into delay. On the other hand, the contractor argues that he is continually in receipt of late design information. The issue is whether the delay is contractor-led through the under-resourcing, or design-led by late design information. A further complication can be that the contractor argues he is resourcing his labour to the level of design information with which he is provided.

'CULPABLE DELAY'

6.65 The concept of culpable delay has been mentioned earlier and only applies to the contractor. The contractor is said to be in culpable delay when the date for completion has passed, the contract has overrun and the contractor is, in the opinion of the contract administrator, not entitled to an extension of time so as to place the completion date in the future.

6.66 It is important to understand the concept of culpable delay because it is often argued that delays to completion caused by the employer or which are at his risk, in a period of culpable delay, have serious consequences for the employer's right to levy liquidated damages. However, this view is erroneous, as discussed in paras. 2.18, 2.19 and 7.38–7.49.

6.67 In practical terms, the assessment of delay is still calculated as explained above. Whether the contractor is in culpable delay or not makes no difference to the delay caused by the event itself. Fig. 15 illustrates the point. The delay caused by this event itself is two calendar days. It is sometimes argued that the delay is fourteen days because the fourteenth day is the earliest date upon which the contractor could have completed the whole of the works as a result of the variation; however, this view has been judicially considered and rejected in *Balfour Beatty Building Ltd. v Chestermount Properties Ltd.* It is correct to add on to the contract period the additional time having regard to the delay caused by the delaying event itself (i.e. the dotting-on principle, see Glossary).

DELAY TO COMPLETION

6.68 Once a delay to an operation or activity has been established, the contract administrator must decide whether that delay causes a delay to completion. A delay on the critical path delays overall completion for the time during which it prevents the start of the next activity on the critical path (see Fig. 10). There may be further consequential delay to operation B in Fig. 10 where the delay to operation A continues and the completion of operation B is dependent on operation A. These situations require monitoring, to establish, for instance, whether the contractor started operation B too early. Clearly, it is for the contractor to organise the sequence of work and he will want to start the next operation as soon as possible: he will not want to be criticised for not using his best endeavours. It may also be that the full extent of any continuing delay to operation A is not apparent when it is decided to commence operation B.

6.69 A delay to an operation on the critical path does not automatically mean that an extension of time must be given for the period of that delay. The criticality of any operation can be established from the sources of information described earlier. Even then, it is only if the delay causes a delay to completion that an extension of time must be considered, and then only if the delay falls within the events recognised by the contract as giving rise to an extension of time.

The award of an extension of time

THE INTERIM AWARD

6.70 JCT 80 requires the contract administrator to fix a new completion date, state which of the relevant events has been taken into account in fixing the new completion date and whether he has taken into account any omission from the works.

6.71 Under GC/Works 1 Edition 3, the PM (contract administrator) awards an extension of time, but there is no express requirement for him to state his reasons. However, clause 35, progress meetings, requires the PM to provide the contractor with a written statement of:

(a) the extent to which he considers the project is on time, delayed or early;

(b) the matters which the PM considers have delayed, or are likely to delay, due completion of the works or any section or sections;

(c) the steps which the PM has agreed with the contractor to reduce or eliminate the effects of any such delay;

(d) the situation in respect of applications for and awards of extensions of time under condition 36 (extensions of time); and

(e) his response to outstanding requests for drawings, nominations, levels or other information.

This provision effectively requires the PM to give the reasons for his award, and to state what he considers is delaying the contract for which no extension is being given.

6.72 Under any form of contract it is good practice to award an extension of time in calendar days, set a new completion date and give the grounds for the award. This would cover what some contracts describe as the interim award, although under GC/Works/1 Edition 3 the PM may state that any award is final rather than interim for the event or events that it covers.

6.73 Contract administrators should always keep notes to show how an award was calculated. This will serve to assist them in the final review and demonstrate, if this is subsequently challenged, how the award was considered and made.

THE FINAL AWARD

6.74 Under JCT 80, the contract administrator is required to make an overall review of delays not later than twelve weeks after practical completion and to consider all relevant events whether notified or not. GC/Works/1 Edition 3 requires the PM to keep all interim decisions under review until he is satisfied he can give a final award.

6.75 If the contract administrator has kept good records and taken proper cognisance of the sources of information available to him, he should have, or be able to compile at practical completion, an as-built programme on which are plotted all the delays.

6.76 The contract administrator should first establish the critical operations and the critical path on the as-built programme. The critical path may have varied from the original, and if this has happened it is important to establish why, because this may have a bearing on the cause or causes of delay. One way to establish the critical path and critical nature of any operation is to work backwards from practical completion. From the contract start date, the delays can then be worked through the as-built programme taking into account what actually happened, not what might have happened or what could have happened, identifying the consequential effects of each delay in turn until the date of practical completion is reached.

6.77 Once the review has been carried out, it should form the basis of the final award. The contract administrator should confirm or increase the extension of time award. At this stage no reduction can be made in an award already given. By the nature of his review, the contract administrator may alter the reasons for his previous awards and, should he do so, should not only state the reason for his increased award, if any, and the relevant events considered, but also the reasons and relevant events considered in reviewing his award.

CONTESTED AWARD

6.78 If the contractor wishes to contest any award made by the contract administrator, the only way for him to do this under the JCT contracts is to proceed to arbitration. GC/Works/1 Edition 3, by contrast, permits the contractor to make a further submission to the PM within fourteen days of the latter's original decision. Should his submission not succeed, the contractor can request adjudication, which is binding on the parties but can be overturned at arbitration. The last resort under all the forms is arbitration.

6.79 In this final forum the contract administrator must be able to respond to the contractor's claims concerning extensions of time and, perhaps more importantly, he should be able to explain the reasons for any extension he has awarded. He can only do this effectively if he has carried out his duties under the contract efficiently and monitored progress of the works in such a way that he can demonstrate what has caused delay to the completion of the contract. A contract administrator who cannot explain why he has made certain awards of extensions of time will have very little credibility.

7 Common problems

Why do Sectional Completion and Partial Possession cause problems?

7.01 Where it is envisaged that there will be phased completion of the works, it is important for the contract administrator to ensure that this is appropriately reflected in the contract documents. If it is not, the extensions of time clause may not be effective, with serious consequences for the employer. Since under the JCT contracts the articles of agreement and conditions take precedence over the other contract documents, it is not sufficient for the necessary provisions to be contained in the bills of quantities alone. This is what had happened in the case of *Gleeson v London Borough of Hillingdon*, where the bills provided that completion should be achieved in sections, but the articles and conditions failed to mention this and no sectional completion supplement was used. The dispute in that case revolved around the liquidated damages clause, and it was held that there was no right to levy liquidated damages when the first of the sections was completed late, because the contractor was not bound to complete that section before the date for practical completion of the whole of the works.

7.02 A contract administrator who has to consider extensions of time has great difficulty in deciding whether he should grant extensions in relation to individual sections or to the works as a whole, if the contract documents do not include all the necessary provisions for the works to be divided into sections. JCT 80, for instance, has a sectional completion supplement which should be used with that form where sectional completion is desired.

7.03 The tendency of the courts has been not to assist the employer in this kind of situation, mainly because liquidated and ascertained damages often feature in these cases and, as these are for the benefit of the employer, the relevant clauses are construed *contra proferentem*, i.e. against his interests where there is any doubt or ambiguity in the wording. An example of this was the case of *Trollope & Colls v North West Metropolitan Regional Hospital Board*, where the parties did include a provision for sectional completion in the contract conditions. Phase III was to start six months after the end of Phase I, an essential arrangement for the hospital, which meant that any extensions of time granted on Phase I would automatically delay the start of Phase III, thus maintaining the required six-month gap. However, the completion of Phase III was not stated in the appendix as a number of weeks after commencement but as an actual date. In the event, the completion of Phase I was 47 weeks later than anticipated; this was for a variety of reasons, some the responsibility of the employer and some for which the contractor was allegedly responsible. In this particular case, the situation worked to the advantage of the contractor, because the delay in commencement of Phase III meant that the contract administrator was unable to find any nominated sub-contractors who could complete the works within the period still remaining for Phase III.

7.04 It might seem reasonable that the court should have implied a term into the contract that if the commencement of work on Phase III was delayed, the completion date for that phase would be extended accordingly. However, the court did not consider it appropriate to do so: first, because the completion date for Phase III in the contract was clear and unambiguous and, secondly, because there was doubt as to what the extended period should be. Should it include, for instance, delays alleged to be caused by the contractor himself?

7.05 This approach was given further support in the later case of *Bruno Zornow v Beechcroft Developments Ltd*, where the extent of the works was massively increased by means of a variation instruction which referred to the phasing of the works without stating completion dates for the phases. The contract administrator clearly had no authority to introduce phased completion into a lump sum contract in any event, even though there was some reference to relevant periods in the tender documents. Again, the court was not prepared to make what it considered to be a fundamental change to the contractual arrangements merely because that seemed to be the most convenient way of dealing with the dispute from the employer's point of view. If the contract is not properly executed, giving separate but linked periods for completion of each phase, the court will provide no assistance in re-drafting or implying terms which would assist in achieving the intended result.

7.06 The situation can become even more complicated when an attempt is made to operate the provisions for partial possession of the works in advance of practical completion. Most standard forms provide that the employer is entitled, with the consent of the contractor, to take parts of the works into his possession before the practical completion date. This is not a substitute for sectional completion, since the contractor is under no obligation to carry out the works in such a way that those sections of the works which the employer wishes to take into possession are completed early. Nevertheless, if partial possession is given to the employer, there is a proportionate reduction in the liquidated and ascertained damages the contractor has to pay if he fails to complete on time. In *Bramall and Ogden v Sheffield City Council* the court was once again strict in interpreting the liquidated and ascertained damages (LADs) clause against the employer, since the wording of the LADs provision – £20 per week for each uncompleted dwelling – was inconsistent with the clause which allowed for partial possession together with a proportionate reduction in the figure for LADs. If the figure used had been the total of £20 x 123 dwellings (the number of houses involved) ie £2,460, there would have been no difficulty in making the proportionate reduction after partial possession.

7.07 As far as extensions of time are concerned, the contract administrator should know that partial possession is usually deemed to be practical completion of the part taken into possession, whatever arrangements are made to finish off the work in that area at a later date. No extensions of time need therefore be considered for any delays relating to those areas after the date of partial possession.

What happens if no extension of time is granted, or an extension is granted late?

7.08 All the standard forms provide for extensions of time to be assessed and granted, if appropriate, by the contract administrator. If the contractor has played his part by giving the requisite notices and supplying information about the delay, the contract administrator is then obliged to consider, within the specified period, whether to grant an extension. If he fails to consider the contractor's notice, he will be in breach of the terms of his own appointment. This might, in turn, put the employer in breach of his implied obligation to provide a person to function as contract administrator under the building contract. If the contract administrator has forgotten that the notice has been served by the contractor or decides to wait and see if the contractor really has been delayed as he alleges, the employer may technically be in breach of contract, which would entitle the contractor to claim damages for that breach.

7.09 It is not clear, however, whether those damages would consist of the loss and expense to which the contractor would have been entitled if the contract administrator had given the relevant extension of time (assuming loss was proved) or whether the failure to grant an extension of time invalidates the practical completion date completely. In that event, the contractor is required to complete only within a reasonable time, taking into account all the circumstances, even those not covered by the extensions of time clause, and without the usual obligation that he should use his 'best endeavours' to avoid or reduce delay.

7.10 Any other method of calculating the loss suffered by the contractor arising from this situation would be difficult to quantify. Loss resulting from the uncertainty as to the practical completion date could be difficult to prove unless it could be linked to acceleration measures specifically intended to deal with the notified delay which the contract administrator had failed to consider.

7.11 There is no case law relating directly to the situation where the contract administrator has deliberately decided not to grant an extension (rather than deciding that no extension is justified) or has forgotten to do so. In the old case of *Miller v LCC* the extensions of time clause was rather different from that in the present standard forms. The engineer in that case had granted an extension of time but not until some months after the works had reached practical completion, and the court held that he was not entitled to do so, on the particular wording of that clause. In the later case, *Amalgamated Building Contractors v Waltham Holy Cross*, Lord Denning held that the *Miller* decision was based on the special wording of the clause, i.e. that it was not generally applicable. Lord Denning's approach was followed in *New Zealand Structures v McKenzie*. The problem would not arise with the modern forms, most of which allow for further extensions to be granted after the practical completion date has passed, on a review of the contract as a whole. It is difficult to see, therefore, how the *Miller* case can assist in considering this issue. In another New Zealand case, *Fernbrook Trading v Taggart*, the issue of a late extension, rather than no extension, was also considered. Having reviewed English, New Zealand and Canadian cases, the judge held that the situation was not particularly clear, and that 'whether the completion date is set at large by a delay in granting an extension must depend upon the particular circumstances pertaining'. One could perhaps extend this comment to a situation where no extension at all has been granted.

7.12 The more recent case of *Temloc v Errill* is also relevant. In that case the contract administrator had not made his final review of extensions within the specified 12-week period, and took 19 weeks to do so. The court said that this was still a valid review of extensions, and that the requirement to carry out this process in 12 weeks was 'directory' only, so there was no breach in failing to meet this deadline. This case has been discussed in more detail in para. 5.22.

7.13 A total failure to review extensions should not arise as often now. Since Amendment 4 of JCT 80, introduced in 1987 and reflected in some of the other JCT contracts, the contract administrator is required to notify the contractor within the specified period either what extension he is giving or that he has considered the notice of delay and does not believe that an extension is justified. These two provisions, coupled with the contract administrator's power to review extensions after practical completion, should give him sufficient scope in dealing with extensions of time; the practice of deferring the granting of extensions until practical completion, to see how the contractor does in fact progress the works, should not be necessary.

Is it essential to comply with the procedural requirements of the extensions of time clause?

7.14 This subject is also covered elsewhere in this book, particularly paras. 5.18, 5.19, 5.23 and 5.24, when considering the detailed requirements of an extensions of time clause. This section is an overview of the question in more general terms.

7.15 The somewhat unhelpful answer to the question whether all the procedural requirements must be strictly followed, is yes and no. The courts have taken a strict view of some of the procedural requirements and a more lenient view of others. For instance, if it is held by a court or arbitrator that a contractor has not served a valid notice of delay, this situation cannot be rectified at a later stage, and the contractor must take the consequences of his failure to give notice as required by the clause (*Merton v Leach*), although this is far less significant now that there is a period of review of extensions after practical completion. On the other hand, where a contract administrator took 19 weeks to review extensions at the end of a contract rather than the specified 12 weeks (*Temloc v Errill*), the court held that this did not make time at large for the purposes of the application of the liquidated and ascertained damages clause. In contrast again, where an extensions of time clause provided a cut-off date for a reference to be made to arbitration if an engineer's decision was disputed, this was applied strictly by the court, even though there was a dispute whether the engineer had given a valid decision so as to start time running for the purposes of the reference to arbitration (*ECC Quarries v Merriman*).

7.16 The rationale behind these apparently conflicting decisions on the question of procedural requirements as to time seems to be that where there are legal consequences arising out of time periods, these will be strictly enforced, whereas if the time periods relate merely to the date by which a certain administrative activity is to be performed they will not be construed so strictly, even when the wording of the clause is that, for instance, 'the architect shall ...'. This can be compared with the approach of the courts to the effect of a final certificate. In most of the JCT forms, a final certificate is conclusive evidence of certain matters, e.g. that all extensions of time which are due under the contract have been given. The exception to this conclusive effect is where arbitration proceedings have been commenced by either party within 28 days of the issue of the final certificate. This time limit has important legal consequences and the courts have taken a strict approach in enforcing it.

7.17 Where there is no case law specifically on the point, it is in the interests of both parties that the procedural requirements be applied with a degree of commonsense. They do, after all, relate to activities on a building site, and are not just a matter for theoretical discussion between barristers (although that can be their fate if a dispute cannot be settled). It is important to bear in mind that the majority of disputes about extensions of time, if they cannot be resolved between the contract administrator and contractor, are submitted to arbitration, and are not, initially at least, subject to review by the courts. Arbitrators in construction disputes are usually experienced practitioners in one of the relevant disciplines, such as quantity surveying or architecture. They, too, are aware that the extensions of time clause must be applied in the context of ongoing work on site, and cannot be considered in isolation.

7.18 Neverthless, if a dispute does arise about extensions of time and it is necessary to refer it to an arbitrator or, possibly, the court, this introduces an element of uncertainty, because a third party has become involved whose own view of the relevant issues may differ from that of either the contract administrator or the contractor. Both sides will be in a stronger position in arguing their case before a court or arbitrator if they have complied with the procedural requirements of the extensions of time clause.

What is the distinction between critical and non-critical delay?

7.19 In assessing delay the contract administrator is concerned with delay which will affect the date set for practical completion, and whether that delay is for reasons which entitle the contractor to an extension of time. Not all activities on site will be on the critical path, although if they are necessary in order to achieve practical completion, they may come on to the critical path at some stage.

7.20 For the purposes of assessing what extension of time should be granted, the contract administrator needs to consider, under some of the standard forms, whether a delay is critical or not. There is an interesting difference here between JCT 80, WCD 81 and IFC 84 on the one hand, which refer to the 'progress of works' being delayed, and the other standard forms discussed in this book (JCT MC 87 and MW 80, GC/Works/1 Edition 3 and GC/Works/2 Edition 2) which refer to a delay to the completion date. In these latter forms, the concepts of critical and non-critical delay are not strictly relevant because the extensions of time clauses refer only to delays which are critical, since they will affect the completion date. This can be a disadvantage because the contractor may wrongly assess a delay as non-critical, and therefore fail to give notice of it.

7.21 The standard forms of sub-contract (apart from the Government form) fall into the former category, i.e. some of the delay to be notified could be non-critical. They are usually more detailed in their requirements, however: they refer to a delay in 'commencement, progress or completion' of the sub-contract works. This fuller wording for sub-contracts may arise because not all sub-contractors will start on site at the date for possession, and because by requiring the notice of delay to contain more detail, the main contractor (or management contractor in the case of MC 87) obtains the type of information which he needs from the sub-contractor in order to assess the overall progress of the works and to enable him to adjust his programme to accommodate delays. It also assists the contractor in making a set-off against other sub-contractors.

7.22 In the case of JCT 80, WCD 81 and IFC 84, the distinction between critical and non-critical delay is important, since it is only critical delay which will affect the completion date, and which needs to be considered in relation to an application for an extension of time. The wording of the relevant clauses in those contracts makes it clear that non-critical delay is to be notified to the contract administrator. In providing information about that delay, however, the contractor can merely say that he does not estimate that there will be any delay in the completion of the works as a result of that particular event, even though it is affecting the progress of the works. It is, of course, part of the contract administrator's responsibility in operating the extensions of time clause to make his own assessment of whether any particular delay notified by the contractor is critical or not. If the cause of the delay is an event which may entitle the contractor to an extension of time but is not likely to delay completion of the works in this particular instance, the contract administrator does not need to take it into consideration in granting any extensions of time. It is nevertheless useful for the contract administrator under these forms of contract to know of non-critical delay, partly because this delay may become critical at a later stage, and partly because it assists in understanding how the works are progressing generally, and therefore how any subsequent variations to the works are likely to affect overall progress.

Does late information from sub-contractors always give rise to an extension of time?

7.23 This is an issue primarily where a sub-contractor has design responsibility but the main contractor does not. In the design and build form, WCD 81, where the main contractor is responsible for design, he is also entirely responsible for the performance of his sub-contractors, and late information from them is his responsibility.

7.24 By contrast in IFC 84, which has a provision for named sub-contractors, the main contractor is expressly exempted from responsibility for their design. He is not, however, entitled to an extension of time for delay by those sub-contractors.

7.25 The issue of late information from sub-contractors comes to the fore more strongly in JCT 80, in relation to nominated sub-contractors. Again, the contractor is expressly exempted from liability for nominated sub-contractors' design (clause 35.21). He is also entitled to an extension of time because of delay by nominated sub-contractors or nominated suppliers 'which the contractor has taken all practicable steps to avoid or reduce'. It should be noted that this ground for an extension does not form a basis for the contractor to claim direct loss and/or expense. If the contractor could, on the other hand, claim that delay by a nominated sub-contractor in providing design drawings fell under the category of late information from the contract administrator (because a contract administrator would normally issue nominated sub-contractors' design drawings as a formal instruction), the contractor would have a ground for claiming direct loss and/or expense.

7.26 There is an implicit acceptance within the JCT 80 documents that a nominated sub-contractor's delay in producing drawings or other information could entitle a contractor to an extension of time on the grounds of late information. The basis for this is that the sub-contractor has an express obligation to the employer under a separate agreement, the direct employer/nominated sub-contractor warranty (NSC/W), to supply information to the contract administrator so as to avoid giving the main contractor a valid claim to an extension of time on the grounds of late information. In that document there is a separate obligation on the nominated sub-contractor not to give the main contractor grounds for an extension of time on account of the nominated sub-contractor's delay generally. Under JCT 80, therefore, it seems fairly clear that if a nominated sub-contractor is late in producing his design drawings, and this delays the contract administrator in issuing the relevant instructions, the contractor may be entitled to an extension of time on the ground of late information.

7.27 This is not the end of the matter, though. In *Fairweather v Wandsworth*, already discussed in para. 4.29, the court made a distinction between design drawings and installation or shop drawings. It was held that an extension of time for late information did not arise in relation to installation drawings prepared by a sub-contractor, since these did not contain design information. That was a decision made by an arbitrator, and upheld by the court, on the basis of the drawings which were in dispute in that particular case. The situation may be different where the installation drawings do contain some design. In *Fairweather* there was also an express obligation that the sub-contractor would be 'responsible for providing all installation drawings in good time to meet the agreed programme for the works'. Since this was part of the sub-contractor's obligations, it was held that it was also part of the main contractor's obligations to the employer.

7.28 In dealing with late information from nominated sub-contractors, the contract administrator must first decide whether the information in question relates to design (in which case it is likely to fall under the category of late instructions to the contractor) or whether it is merely a question of installation details (which will usually remain the responsibility of the contractor as set out in *Fairweather v Wandsworth*). This can be a difficult distinction to make. Under JCT 80, the main contractor has an obligation to take 'all practicable steps' to avoid or reduce delay by nominated sub-contractors, and therefore has responsibility for his nominated sub-contractors' progress, both in terms of the works themselves and drawings and other information to be produced by the nominated sub-contractors as part of their sub-contract. It is not absolutely clear whether this also includes design information produced by the nominated sub-contractor. If the analysis above is correct, the contractor is not responsible for the timing of the production of such information.

Could an instruction to rectify defective work entitle the contractor to an extension of time?

7.29 It could, depending upon the exact terms of the contract. The question arises because unless there is a provision allowing the contract administrator to issue such instructions without time consequences, the instruction may be treated as a variation, which will entitle the contractor to an extension of time. In general terms, if the contractor carries out defective work, the contract administrator will usually have the power to order its removal from site. The contractor still has the obligation to complete the work and must therefore replace the defective work with new, satisfactory, work. In some cases, however, it is not practical to use exactly the same design because of the nature of the work itself (e.g. foundation work), and the contract administrator may then find himself issuing instructions which are later interpreted as variations, with the time consequences which follow from that. This is exactly what happened in the case of *Simplex v London Borough of St Pancras*, which concerned the pre-1963 version of the JCT contract. There was a problem with the piling, which on testing was found to be inadequate to take the required loads. The contractor wrote to the contract administrator with two suggested alternative ways of dealing with the difficulty, adding, 'we shall be glad to have your instructions and views as to the extra cost which will be involved'. The contract administrator responded initially by telephone and then confirmed by letter that he was prepared to accept the contractor's proposal for one of the alternatives which had been suggested. Even though the contract administrator did not use the word 'instruction' in his letter, it was held that an instruction for a variation had been issued and that the normal consequences of a variation instruction would therefore follow.

7.30 One way of avoiding a variation instruction, when this kind of situation occurs, is to go right outside the terms of the building contract and make a separate agreement between employer and contractor as to what remedial works are necessary and the time it will take to carry them out, without prejudice to any later claims which either party might wish to bring against the other in relation to the defective work. This is how the situation was covered in the case of *Costain v Howard de Walden*. The court agreed that there had been no variation instruction, and that issues of time and extra cost were to be governed by the separate agreement.

7.31 The difficulties for the contract administrator in dealing with work which does not conform to the building contract have been considerably eased by the introduction of an amplified clause 8 in JCT 80, which gives the contract administrator many more options when this situation arises. He can, for instance, allow work which is not in accordance with the contract to remain, and issue consequential instructions without those instructions being construed as variations which would entitle the contractor to an extension of time. When a problem of this kind arises in practice, it is essential to establish precisely which version of a contract is being used, and which amendments have been incorporated into it, so that the extended powers under clause 8 can be implemented where appropriate. Similar amendments have been made to WCD 81. MC 87 still uses the earlier wording, which entitles the contract administrator to instruct the removal from site of work which is not in accordance with the contract, and to open up for inspection any work covered up, or arrange for testing to be carried out. The extended powers now available to the contract administrator under JCT 80 are not, however, open to a contract administrator under MC 87, unless the equivalent of Amendment 5 to JCT 80 has been incorporated into it.

7.32 The wording of the relevant clauses in IFC 84 and MW 80 is different, and the contract administrator is more limited in the actions he can take before he encounters the difficulties which faced the contract administrator in the *Simplex* case. As one would expect, the Government forms deal with the issue of defective work in a comprehensive manner, which avoids the *Simplex* problem arising. Clearly, it is not in the employer's interests that the rectification of defective work should entitle the contractor to an extension of time, and there is a general rule that a party to a contract should not be entitled to take advantage of his own breach of that contract. Nevertheless, in the case of some of the standard forms of building contract, particularly those where the right to issue instructions to deal with defective work is limited, the contract administrator may find that he has issued a variation instruction merely by agreeing to the contractor's proposal for rectifying the work. In the *Simplex* case the court found it 'not immaterial' that the contract administrator thought the employer might be liable for the costs of the extra piling, i.e. the contract administrator thought that he was obliged to issue a variation instruction in the circumstances. If a contract administrator's view is that the employer should not be liable in this way, he should, at the very least, make sure that the contractor is fully aware of this fact.

Should the construction programme be a contract document?

7.33 This question arises because if the programme is considered a contract document, it may give rise to an implication that any failure to comply with its requirements on the part of either the contractor, or the contract administrator on behalf of the employer, will be a breach of contract. This is particularly important where the programme gives the dates by which certain information is required from the contract administrator, and those dates are not met. The programme can in those circumstances be of considerable assistance to the contractor in alleging delay on the ground of late information. This would only apply, of course, if such information was on the critical path. If it is shown in that position, and the contract administrator has approved or otherwise accepted the programme as an accurate assessment of the information contained on it, he will be in a weak position if he wishes to argue, at a later stage, that the information requested is not in fact critical at that date.

7.34 From the point of view of the contractor, if the construction programme is a contract document, he may be in breach of contract if he does not complete all the various activities shown on the programme by the designated dates. In those contracts where the programme is a contract document there is usually no sanction of liquidated damages if the contractor fails to comply with the interim dates and activities shown on his programme. In theory at least, though, the employer could claim from the contractor damages for breach of contract if he could prove that he had suffered a specific loss which was reasonably within the contemplation of the parties when the contract was made, as a result of the contractor's failure to meet the interim dates.

7.35 The use of a construction programme in relation to applications for extensions of time is covered in some detail in paras. 6.06–6.13. The programme is undoubtedly a helpful tool to the contract administrator in making his assessment. This will be particularly so if the contract administrator has, at the outset of the contract, considered whether the programme is realistic in the light of the work which has to be carried out.

7.36 The major Government form, GC/Works/1 Edition 3, provides that the programme is a contract document and describes in some detail what it must contain. Clearly, it is possible to operate a contract in which the programme is a contract document, with all the restrictions which that implies on both contractor and contract administrator. The reason why it is not normally made a contract document, in the JCT forms for instance, is simply that it is restrictive on the contract administrator and that it can operate so as to relieve the contractor from his obligation to determine his own method of working and to reorganise the works when necessary so as to avoid delay where this is possible.

7.37 Where a programme sets out the dates by which the contract administrator is to provide certain information, it was held in *Merton v Leach* that the programme could operate as a notice of delay. It cannot, however, go as far as to oblige the contract administrator to provide information earlier than is necessary to enable the contractor to complete the works by the contractual completion date (*Glenlion v Guinness Trust*). If, therefore, the contractor produces a programme, whether or not it is a contract document, which shows completion earlier than the contractual date for completion and also shows dates by which information is required from the contract administrator, this document cannot of itself form a notice of delay for the purposes of a claim for an extension of time. The contract administrator in this situation must consider carefully when, in his view, that information will become crucial for the contractor, and provide it by that date in order to avoid a claim for late information. This is not an easy assessment to make, since it involves the contract administrator in virtually writing his own programme, complete with critical path, which he is not generally equipped to do.

What happens when a 'neutral' delay occurs if the contractor is already in default?

7.38 As explained in para. 3.12, neutral events are those which are not caused by either party, but which may entitle the contractor to an extension of time, e.g. exceptionally adverse weather. When using some of the older standard forms of contract, such as JCT 63, the question sometimes arose whether, after the completion date had passed, the contract administrator had any power at all to extend the time for completion. This issue arose because of the particular wording of JCT 63. In the later forms the wording is different and the contract administrator not only has the power to review extensions within a certain period after practical completion but can also grant an extension to the contractor for neutral events which occur during a period of default before practical completion. This was the view of Lord Denning in *Amalgamated Building Contractors v Waltham Holy Cross*, although the High Court judge in the more recent case of *Balfour Beatty Building Ltd. v Chestermount Properties Ltd.* cast some doubt on this. There is not much scope therefore for argument on this point in relation to the wording of JCT 80. The clearest wording occurs in IFC 84.

7.39 If the contract administrator does have power to consider and grant an extension of time for delay during the period of the contractor's default, is the delay to be added to the existing completion date or is the contractor also entitled to an extension of time up to and including the delaying event? In this section neutral events only are being considered. The question was considered in the *Amalgamated Building Contractors* case where Lord Denning mentioned as an example the situation where the contractor had been in culpable delay for six months. If at that stage a strike occurred which lasted a month, the contract administrator could extend time by one month from the original completion date, even though the new completion date would still be a date which had already passed. This was also confirmed, after a more detailed analysis, in the *Balfour Beatty* case. Similarly, where delay has been caused by a nominated sub-contractor in circumstances which do not entitle the contractor to an extension of time, if the sub-contractor then becomes insolvent and the architect delays in appointing a new sub-contractor, the contractor will still be entitled to an extension of time for that delay, although not for the nominated sub-contractor's original delay (*Percy Bilton v GLC*).

Can the contract administrator issue a variation instruction while the contractor is in culpable delay?

7.40 The question envisages that the completion date for the project has passed but the works have not yet reached practical completion. Since most of the standard forms provide that the contract administrator shall, before the completion date is reached, give whatever extensions he considers are due to the contractor, the fact that the works are not practically complete should mean that this is due to a default on the part of the contractor. If, at this stage in the contract, the contract administrator issues a variation instruction, is the contract administrator entitled to grant whatever further extension of time is relevant in relation to that instruction and, if so, must the extension be granted up to the date on which the variation can be carried out?

7.41 The first point to note is that there is nothing in the standard forms which restricts the contract administrator's power to issue instructions before practical completion has been achieved, even if this happens in a period when the contractor is in culpable delay.

7.42 The contractor will argue that he could not have completed the works by the due date since the works as finally constructed include the extra work ordered, and a variation instruction for the extra items which would subsequently form part of the works was not issued until after that date. One response which is often given, on behalf of contract administrators, is that the contractor was not ready to deal with the variation, e.g. some minor amendment to the finishes, until the date on which the instruction was issued, and that if the contractor had been working to programme the variation would have been instructed earlier. There is no case law directly on this point where the variation does not actually cause any delay to the contractor. On the basis of the recent *Balfour Beatty* judgment (discussed below), however, there is no reason why, if the variation does not cause delay, it should invalidate the contractual provisions regarding extensions of time and liquidated and ascertained damages, by putting time at large.

7.43 Where a variation is instructed during a period of culpable delay and the variation does delay the contractor, there have been several cases which have established the principle that:

> 'the ordering of variations after the due date which must substantially delay completion will, unless the contract provides otherwise, and in the absence of an applicable extensions of time clause, disable the [employer] from recovering or retaining liquidated damages which might otherwise have accrued after the giving of the order, the employer's right in respect of amounts that have already accrued by way of liquidated damages not being affected.' (*SMK Cabinets v Hili Modern Electrics*)

7.44 This Australian decision was referred to with approval in the recent English case of *McAlpine Humberoak v McDermott International*. It seems clear, therefore, that where an instruction which will cause substantial delay is issued during this period, any accrued rights to liquidated damages which the employer has should not be affected. However, there is a difficulty. When the contract administrator extends time, he adds the appropriate period of time to the existing completion date, and this could have the effect of extending the completion date so far that part or all of the period for which the employer would otherwise be able to levy LADs was included in the extended period and the employer would thereby lose his right to LADs. The court in both *SMK Cabinets* and *Humberoak* did not appear to have appreciated this fact. The mechanism of the granting of extensions could therefore reduce or completely destroy the employer's accrued rights to LADs.

7.45 In *Humberoak* there was no provision for liquidated damages, and the court did not therefore have to deal with the question of what happens to liquidated damages from the date the variation instruction is issued. In *SMK Cabinets*, where there was a provision for liquidated damages but no extensions of time clause, the court held that they were not recoverable. The various cases on this subject, both Australian and English, were considered and it was reaffirmed that, in the context of 'substantial delay' to completion caused partly by the employer and partly by the contractor, the employer will no longer be entitled to liquidated damages for the period after the delaying instruction, unless the extensions of time clause allows for an appropriate extension to be made.

7.46 The contract administrator is not primarily concerned with the question of liquidated damages, although clearly he would not wish to take a step which would disentitle his client from claiming liquidated damages if appropriate. The *Balfour Beatty* case considered the consequences of issuing a variation instruction when the contractor was in culpable delay and looked in some detail at the arguments on both sides. The contract in that case was an amended version of JCT 80, but this does not affect the crucial issues. The judge held that the wording of the extensions of time clause was wide enough in its natural meaning to include relevant events occurring before or after the completion date. Risk had been allocated between the parties for relevant events which occurred before the completion date, and the judge found it most improbable that it was intended to introduce a very different allocation of risk for relevant events occurring after the completion date. In the *Humberoak* case the Court of Appeal had held:

'If a contractor is already a year late through his culpable fault, it would be absurd that the employer should lose his claim for unliquidated damages just because, at the last moment, he orders an extra coat of paint.'

7.47 In the *Balfour Beatty* case the judge followed this line of argument and said that it could not be the common intention of the parties that a trivial variation instruction, issued after a lengthy period of delay by the contractor, would mean that the employer lost all his right to liquidated damages for the entire period of culpable delay, up to the date on which that variation was carried out or even up to practical completion itself.

7.48 The judge considered the argument that the contract was ambiguous on this point, and that the court should therefore apply the *contra proferentem* rule, i.e. to interpret the clause against the interests of the employer, since the liquidated damages clause, which is clearly dependent on the extensions of time clause, is for the benefit of the employer. The judge held, however, that the contract was not so ambiguous or unclear that the *contra proferentem* rule should be applied.

7.49 The Court in the *Balfour Beatty* case also went on to say that if an extension of time was warranted, following this kind of variation instruction, the contractor would not be entitled to an extension up to the date on which the variation could be carried out. The fair and reasonable time for the extension should merely be added to the existing completion date (i.e. the dotting-on principle).

How should concurrent delay be assessed?

7.50 The previous two sections have dealt with different types of delay which occur at the same time as the contractor is also in culpable delay, i.e. the completion date has passed but practical completion has not yet been achieved. In this section, the situation to be considered is one where two competing causes of delay have occurred, both of which are covered by the extension of time clause but only one of which entitles the contractor to extra payment for direct loss and/or expense. An extension of time is not, of course, an automatic pre-condition to further payment for the contractor, although there is a connection in some circumstances. It is important for a contractor, for instance under JCT 80, to know whether an extension of time has been granted for exceptionally adverse weather conditions or because of late information, since the consequences will be different when making a claim for extra payment.

7.51 The extensions of time clauses in the various standard forms do not expressly require the contract administrator to state what time has been allocated to a particular event; merely, in some of the forms, which relevant events have been taken into account. Nevertheless, in order to make the appropriate ascertainment of direct loss and/or expense, both contractor and quantity surveyor need to know what time has been allocated to each of the relevant events which the contract administrator has taken into account.

7.52 In the minor standard forms this is not an issue. JCT MW 80 requires a contract administrator to give such extension of time as is fair and reasonable in the circumstances, and the contractor is not entitled to any further payment arising out of an extension as such – only where a variation has affected the regular progress of the works. It is in the major forms that the problem arises.

7.53 The courts have been called upon to consider this issue on several occasions, not with reference to building contracts but in the context of damage to shipping, particularly during the 1939–45 war. If the damage had been caused by 'perils at sea' this could be covered by the appropriate insurance policy. However, if the damage was caused by 'warlike activities', this would fall within one of the exceptions to an insurance policy. In *Leyland Shipping v Norwich Union,* a ship had been torpedoed and subsequently broke up in heavy seas just outside the harbour where it had been taken for repair. In another case, *Yorkshire Dale*, the ship had been stranded partly because of the route chosen by the navigator in order to avoid enemy submarines, and partly because there was an unusual tidal set which had taken the ship too close to the rocks around the Outer Hebrides. Those cases are, naturally, not relevant in their detail, although the judges did make some more general remarks about this type of situation where an accident has been caused by more than one cause. In *Yorkshire Dale*, one of the Law Lords said :

'One has to ask oneself what was the effective and predominant cause of the accident that happened, whatever the nature of that accident may be.'

In the same case, another of the Law Lords expressed it slightly differently:

'Each case must be judged in the light of its own facts and by resorting, not to the refinements of the philosophical doctrine of causation, but to the commonplace tests which the ordinary businessman conversant with such matters would adopt.'

In reaching a decision in that case, the judges referred to the 'predominant and determining cause' of the accident, and came to their decision on that basis.

7.54 The 'dominant cause' approach therefore seems to be the one favoured by the House of Lords. It must be borne in mind, however, that in the cases mentioned above neither of the two competing causes would have been sufficient in themselves to cause the total loss of the vessel. Two concurrent relevant events under the major JCT forms might each be a sufficient cause, on their own, to cause delay. For instance, either exceptionally adverse weather conditions or late information from the contract administrator could logically operate on their own so as to cause delay. It could be argued, therefore, that the shipping cases are not directly relevant to this question.

7.55 There are differing views among the writers of legal textbooks in the construction field as to the correct approach to be taken. Max Abrahamson, for instance, suggests that it is for the contractor to prove which of the various causes of delay was the 'operative cause' (*Engineering Law and the ICE Contracts* 4th Edition p370). In the fifth (1991) edition of *Keating on Building Contracts*, by contrast, the dominant cause approach is taken to be the correct one.

7.56 It is perhaps surprising that there is no case in which this point has been decided by the courts. In *Fairweather v Wandsworth* the question was considered in relation to the combined effect of strikes and variation instructions. The judge pointed out that an extension of time is not a condition precedent to the right to recover direct loss and/or expense, and that in relation to variation instructions, associated direct loss and/or expense can be recovered under the variation clause whether or not an extension of time has also been granted. (This was a case on the JCT 63 form and this point would not necessarily apply to JCT 80.) It was not therefore relevant or necessary for him to deal with the fact that the arbitrator had, in considering competing causes of delay, held that the dominant cause of delay was the one for which the contract administrator should grant the extension. The judge nevertheless went on to consider this matter and said that he did not consider that the dominant test was correct. He did not, however, give any reasons for that conclusion, which was, strictly speaking, *obiter dictum* (see Glossary). It is no doubt for this reason that the editor of *Keating* has chosen to follow the shipping cases, rather than *Fairweather v Wandsworth*, in the consideration of concurrent causes of delay. It is also worth noting that in *Fairweather* the contract in question was JCT 63, and that the wording of the JCT 80 extensions of time clause is slightly different.

7.57 For the contract adminstrator, the situation is not satisfactory. In some instances, he will be able to assess what was the dominant cause of delay, and grant extensions of time accordingly; in others, it may be extremely difficult to make that assessment. Various suggestions have been put forward in the building press from time to time of practical ways of dealing with the direct loss and/or expense to which the contractor might be entitled following an extension of time where there has been concurrent delay, usually on the basis of some kind of apportionment of the delay between the competing causes. The major JCT forms neither support nor prohibit those practical approaches. There is further discussion on the ways in which a contract administrator can make his allocation of extensions in paras. 6.55–6.64.

If the contractor's own delay puts critical work into a season of inclement weather, is the contractor entitled to an extension of time?

7.58 The situation envisaged here is that when work started on site it was reasonable to assume that crucial elements, such as groundworks or completing the watertight envelope of the building, would be finished before the winter period, but that because of the contractor's own delay that work had not been completed before the onset of winter. The works are nevertheless still within the contract period. If at this stage there is exceptionally inclement weather which delays the contractor, is he entitled to an extension of time?

7.59 On behalf of the employer, it can be argued that if the contractor had not been in delay, the exceptionally inclement weather would not have delayed him because the critical elements of the work would have been completed before that delaying event. In *Walter Lawrence v Commercial Union*, discussed in para. 4.06, the court held that the assessment of whether or not the contractor had been delayed by exceptionally inclement weather must be made in relation to the work being carried out by the contractor at the time of the inclement weather conditions, and not by reference to the work which he ought to have been carrying out by that stage of the contract period.

7.60 In assessing whether there has been exceptionally inclement weather, however, the contract administrator must compare the weather actually experienced with that which is normal for the time of year. It is not a question of making a comparison with the type of weather which the contractor could have expected had he been completing the work at the earlier, programmed, time.

What does 'best endeavours' mean?

7.61 The phrase 'best endeavours' is often used in the context of an extensions of time clause; the contractor is required to use his best endeavours to prevent delay or further delay. The cases in which the phrase has been considered by the courts are not construction cases, but they are nevertheless a useful indication of what is involved in undertaking an obligation to use best endeavours. The obligation does not, for instance, extend so far as to require a party to act fraudulently, or to violate the terms of another contract (*Monkland v Jack Barclay*).

7.62 The phrase does, nevertheless, imply the expenditure of money. In the case of *IBM v Rockware Glass*, Rockware agreed to sell IBM some land for development, and one of the conditions of sale was that IBM 'will make an application for planning permission and use its best endeavours to obtain the same'. The local authority refused planning permission. IBM did not appeal against that decision to the Secretary of State. The parties disagreed on whether, by not appealing, IBM had failed to use its best endeavours to obtain planning permission.

7.63 The project was a substantial one, in which the purchase price of the land alone was £6,250,000. It was accepted that making an appeal to the Secretary of State would cost a significant amount of money. The court said that taking into account the background of the case and the amount of money involved, it was not likely that the parties would have considered a refusal of planning permission at a local level to be the end of the matter, but that they must have had in mind the prospect of an appeal to the Secretary of State. The test of best endeavours which was approved in that case was that the purchasers of the land 'are bound to take all those steps in their power which are capable of producing the desired results, namely the obtaining of planning permission, being steps which a prudent, determined and reasonable owner, acting in his own interests and desiring to achieve that result, would take'. It was expressly stated that the criterion was not that of someone who was under a contractual obligation but someone who was considering his own interests.

7.64 Putting the decision into a construction context, the exercise of best endeavours is clearly a significant requirement which could go beyond the mere reorganisation of resources in order to mitigate delay. If a contractor was 'considering his own interests' in a situation where there had been delay (for example, if the contractor himself was likely to suffer financially because of the delay), he would make considerable efforts in order to prevent or avoid delay. Where delay had occurred, he might well consider the use of extra resources, i.e. spending money, in order to prevent any further delay.

7.65 In a somewhat earlier case, *Sheffield District Railway Company v Great Central Railway Company*, the dispute was about the use of best endeavours to develop traffic on the Sheffield railway. In that case the obligation was expressed slightly differently. The court said that the words did not mean second-best endeavours. 'They do not mean that the limits of reason must be overstepped with regard to the cost of the service ... but .... that [the defendants] must, broadly speaking, leave no stone unturned'. Here again, the expenditure of money in order to satisfy the obligation to use best endeavours was clearly envisaged.

7.66 It would therefore seem that the obligation on the contractor to use his best endeavours means that he must put his whole-hearted efforts into reorganising the work so as to avoid further delay, as if it was directly in his own interests to do so, and 'leaving no stone unturned'. The contractor should also, as part of this exercise, consider what steps might be taken to prevent delay even if these involve extra expense on his part, on the basis that this could be recovered as part of a claim for disruption. If the amount involved was considerable, however, a prudent contractor would no doubt wish to inform the professional team, at the least, of his proposals. At the same time, the obligation to use best endeavours cannot be equated with an obligation to accelerate, for which the standard contracts, with the exception of JCT MC 87 and GC/Works/1 Edition 3, have no provision.

7.67 The extensions of time clause usually provides for extensions in a variety of circumstances, some of which are neutral events such as bad weather and some of which are the responsibility of the employer, such as variations, delay in supplying free issue materials etc. In these latter cases there are usually provisions elsewhere in the contract for reimbursement to the contractor if there is delay, but a contractor may still be put to extra irrecoverable expense in complying with the best endeavours obligation.

7.68 Where the contractor himself has caused the delay, he must of course overcome it at his own expense or be liable for liquidated damages in accordance with the terms of the contract.

7.69 The position where a neutral event (see para. 3.12) has caused delay is more difficult, because there is usually no provision in the contract for payment to the contractor if he spends money in mitigating that type of delay. The obligation on the contractor to use his best endeavours to avoid delay nevertheless remains, and there is no indication in the wording of these clauses that best endeavours means something different in relation to neutral events. The contractor must therefore be considered to have priced the risk of delay for neutral events in his original tender, including the extra costs of dealing with any delay under the best endeavours clause.

Table of cases

Amalgamated Building Contractors Ltd. v Waltham Holy Cross U.D.C. (1952) 2 ALL ER 452

Balfour Beatty Building Ltd. v Chestermount Properties Ltd. (1993) 9 Const LJ 117

Boskalis Westminster Construction Ltd. v Liverpool City Council (1983) 24 BLR 83

Bramall and Ogden Ltd. v Sheffield City Council (1983) 29 BLR 73

Bruno Zornow (Builders) Ltd. v Beechcroft Developments Ltd (1989) 16 Con LR 30

Computer & Systems Engineering Plc v John Lelliott (Ilford) Ltd. (1991) CILL 673

Costain Management Design Ltd. v Howard de Walden Estates Ltd. (1991) 55 BLR 124

Croudace Ltd. v London Borough of Lambeth (1986) 33 BLR 20

ECC Quarries Ltd. v Merriman Ltd. (1988) 45 BLR 90

Fernbrook Trading Company Ltd. v Taggart (1979) 1 NZLR 556

GLC v Cleveland Bridge & Engineering Co. Ltd. (1986) 34 BLR 50

Gleeson (Contractors) Ltd. v London Borough of Hillingdon (1970) 215 EG 165

Glenlion Construction Ltd. v Guinness Trust (1987) 39 BLR 89

H Fairweather & Co. Ltd. v London Borough of Wandsworth (1987) 39 BLR 106

Holland Hannen & Cubbits (N) Ltd. v Welsh Health TSO (1981) 18 BLR 80

Humber Oils Terminal Trustees Ltd. v Hersent Offshore Ltd. (1981) 20 BLR 16

IBM UK Ltd. v Rockware Glass Ltd. (1980) FSR 335

J & J Fee Ltd. v Express Lift Co. Ltd. (1993) (unreported)

Kitsons Sheet Metal Ltd. v Matthew Hall M & E Engineers Ltd. (1989) 47 BLR 82

Leyland Shipping Co. Ltd. v Norwich Union Fire Insurance Society Ltd. (1918) AC 350

London Borough of Hounslow v Twickenham Garden Developments Ltd. (1970) 7 BLR 81

London Borough of Merton v Leach Ltd. (1985) 32 BLR 57

Martin Grant & Co. Ltd. v Sir Lindsay Parkinson (1984) 3 Con LR 12

Matsoukis v Priestman (1915) 1 KB 681

McAlpine Humberoak Ltd. v McDermott International Inc. (1992) 58 BLR 1

Miller v London County Council [1934] ALL ER 657

Monkland v Jack Barclay Ltd (1951) 1 ALL ER 714

Neodox Ltd. v Borough of Swinton & Pendlebury (1958) 5 BLR 34

New Zealand Structures & Investments Ltd. v McKenzie (1979) 1 NZLR 515

Peak Construction (Liverpool) Ltd. v McKinney Foundations Ltd. (1970) 1 BLR 111

Percy Bilton Ltd. v GLC (1982) 17 and 20 BLR 1

Perini v Commonwealth of Australia (1969) 12 BLR 82

SMK Cabinets v Hili Modern Electrics Pty Ltd. (1984) VR 391

Sheffield District Railway Company v Great Central Railway Company (1911) 27 TLR 451

Simplex Concrete Piles Ltd. v London Borough of St Pancras (1958) 14 BLR 80

Surrey Heath Borough Council v Lovell Construction Ltd. (1988) 42 BLR 25

Temloc Ltd. v Errill Properties Ltd. (1987) 39 BLR 30

Trollope & Colls Ltd. v North West Metropolitan Regional Hospital Board [1973] 2 ALL ER 260

Walter Lawrence & Son Ltd. v Commercial Union Properties (UK) Ltd. (1984) 4 Con LR 37

Yorkshire Dale (1942) AC 691

Abbreviations

ALL ER	All England Reports
Const LJ	Construction Law Journal
BLR	Building Law Reports
Con LR	Construction Law Reports
CILL	Construction Industry Law Letter
NZLR	New Zealand Law Reports
EG	Estates Gazette
FSR	Fleet Street Reports
AC	Appeal Cases
KB	King's Bench
VR	Victoria Reports (Australia)
TLR	Times Law Reports

Index